JUNIOR PUZZLE FUN

BOOK 4

Published by
Grandreams Limited.
435-437 Edgware Road,
Little Venice,
London, W2 1TH.

Printed in Hungary.

Solutions to these puzzles can be found at the back of this book

STARTING AT THE LETTER "W", MOVE FROM ONE SQUARE TO THE NEXT, TO FIND THE NAMES OF SIX SEA ANIMALS. USE EACH SQUARE ONLY ONCE
S H L H W
I C E A L
F R E S E
L A B H A
A E S K R
1

2

AEROPLANE JUMBLE

1 LDUCO

2 NSU

3 DIRB

4 NIAR

5 EOHUS

6 WCO

7 ERTE

8 IVRER

Can you name these jumbled-up things that the man can see from his aeroplane?

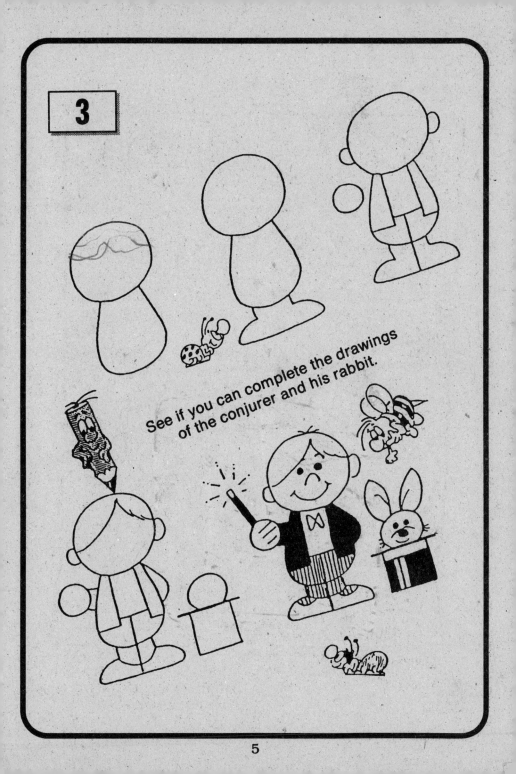

3
See if you can complete the drawings
of the conjurer and his rabbit.

Can you spot ten differences between the two pictures?

4

5

Using the pictures as clues, fill in the answers and discover a word hidden in the circled squares reading diagonally.

6

Which path links our two friends?

Which shadow matches the cow's bell?

8
Silly me. I buried some money in my garden a long while ago, but I just can't remember where I've hidden it. I've been digging tunnels to try to find it. Can you help me ?
A
B
C
D
E

COLOUR-IN
9

10

Join the dots and complete the picture.

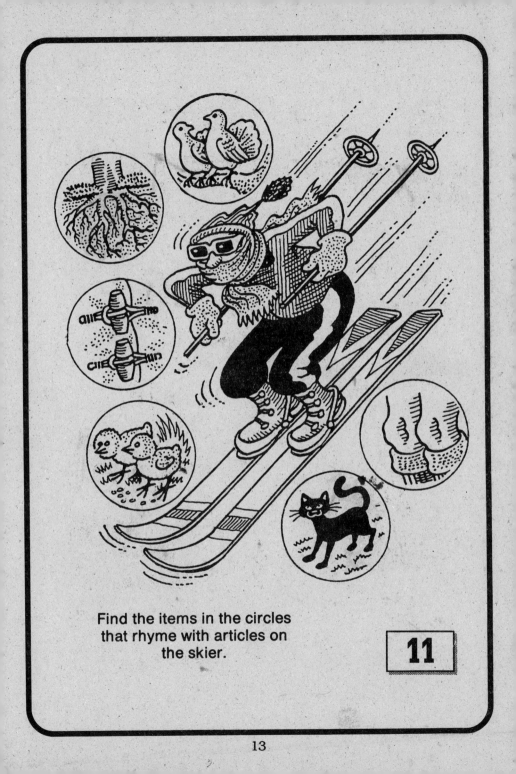

Find the items in the circles that rhyme with articles on the skier.

11

Can you find the ten pencils in this picture?
12
M
M

13

Pair the sports off.

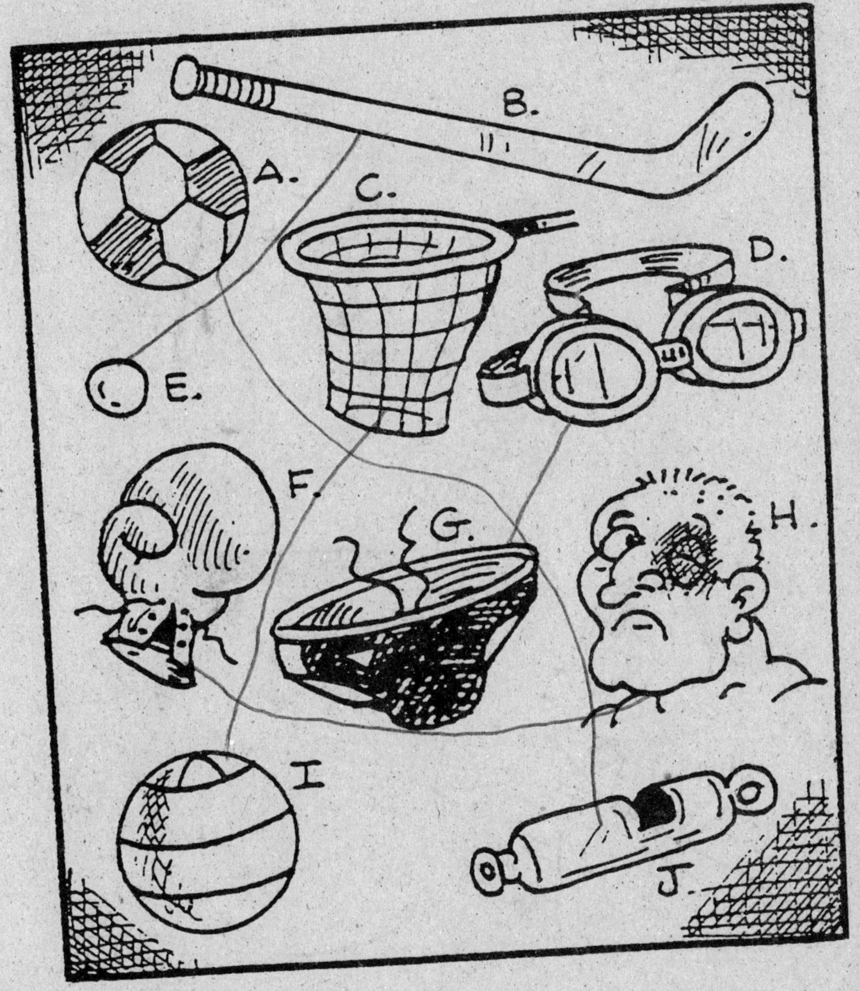

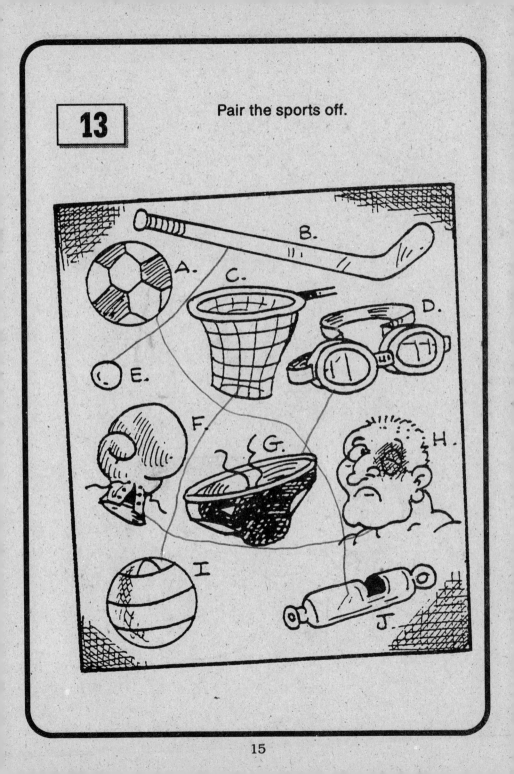

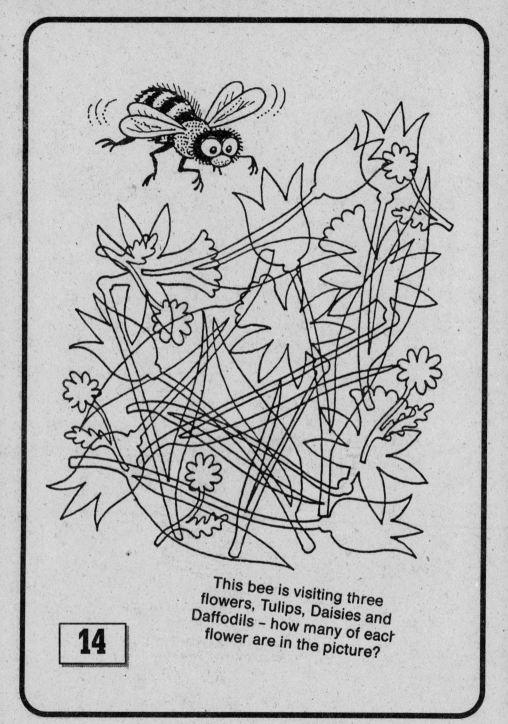

This bee is visiting three flowers, Tulips, Daisies and Daffodils – how many of each flower are in the picture?

14

15

Using the pictures as clues, fill in the answers and discover a hidden word in the circled squares reading diagonally.

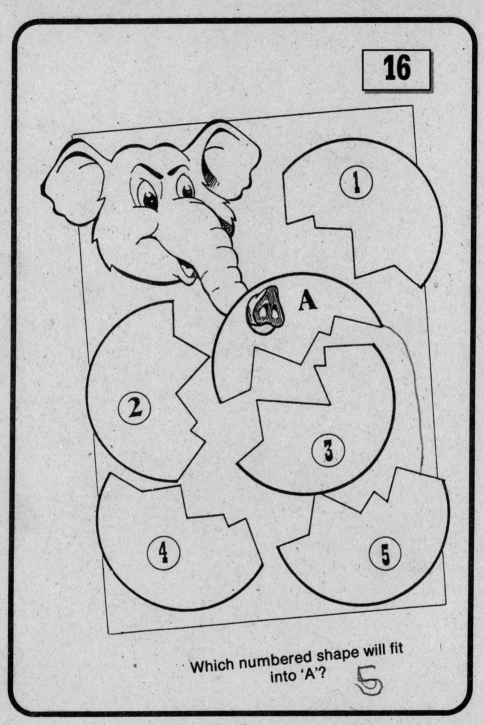

16

Which numbered shape will fit into 'A'?

17

Remove three ice-creams to make three squares.

Draw the little gnome who has just finished building a snowman. Try to complete the two unfinished drawings.
18

19

Follow the Nursery Rhyme Trail – each word begins with a large letter.

20

21

Which rope does the climber pull to help him reach the clifftop?

22

Find two numbers which only appear five times. Add them together to find the distance jumped.

RE-ARRANGE THE LETTERS TO SPELL OUT FIVE WORDS!

23

24

What sort of games can this lad choose to play?

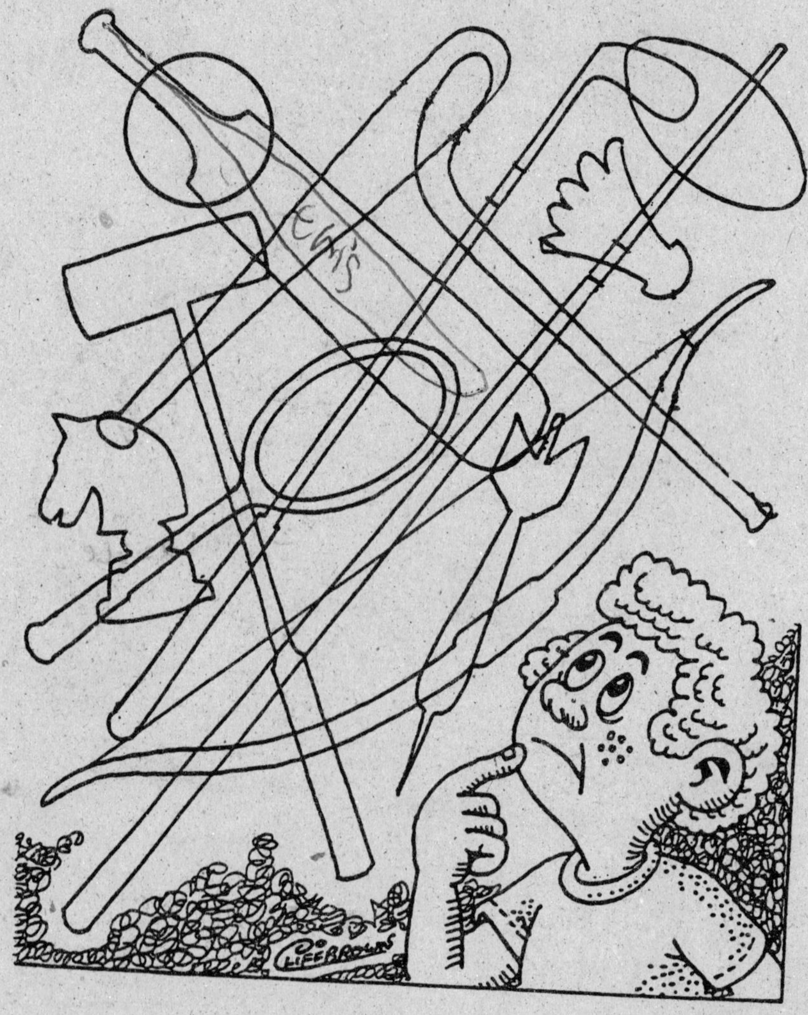

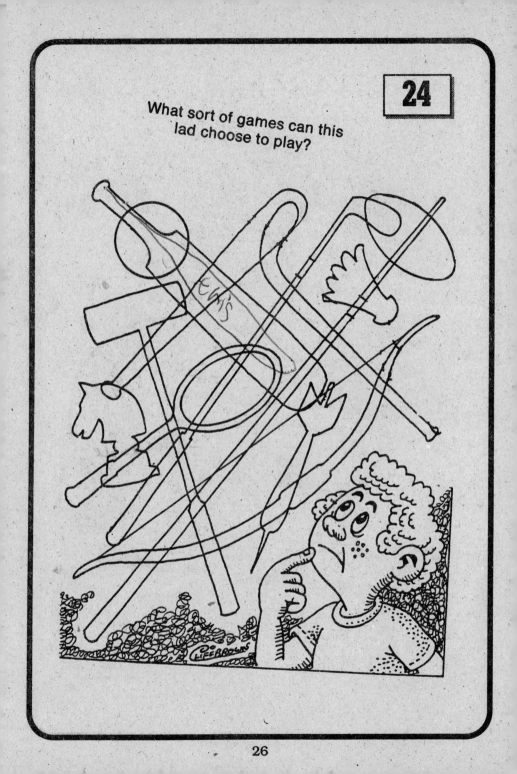

25

Can you find the words hidden in the grid?

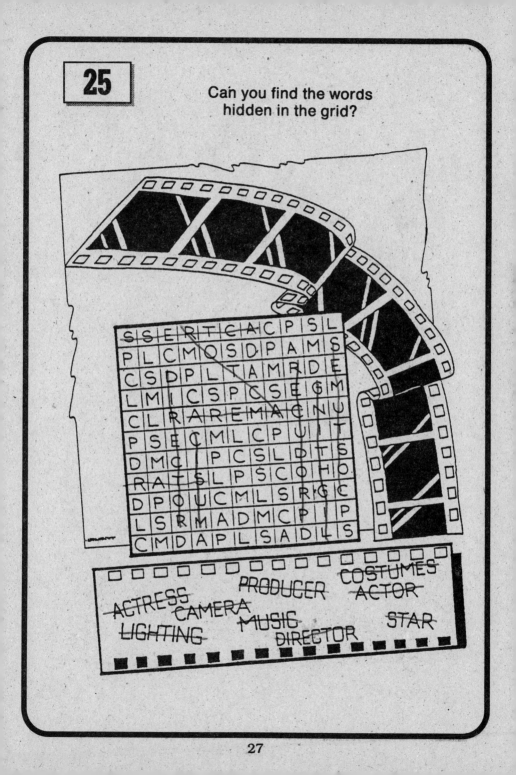

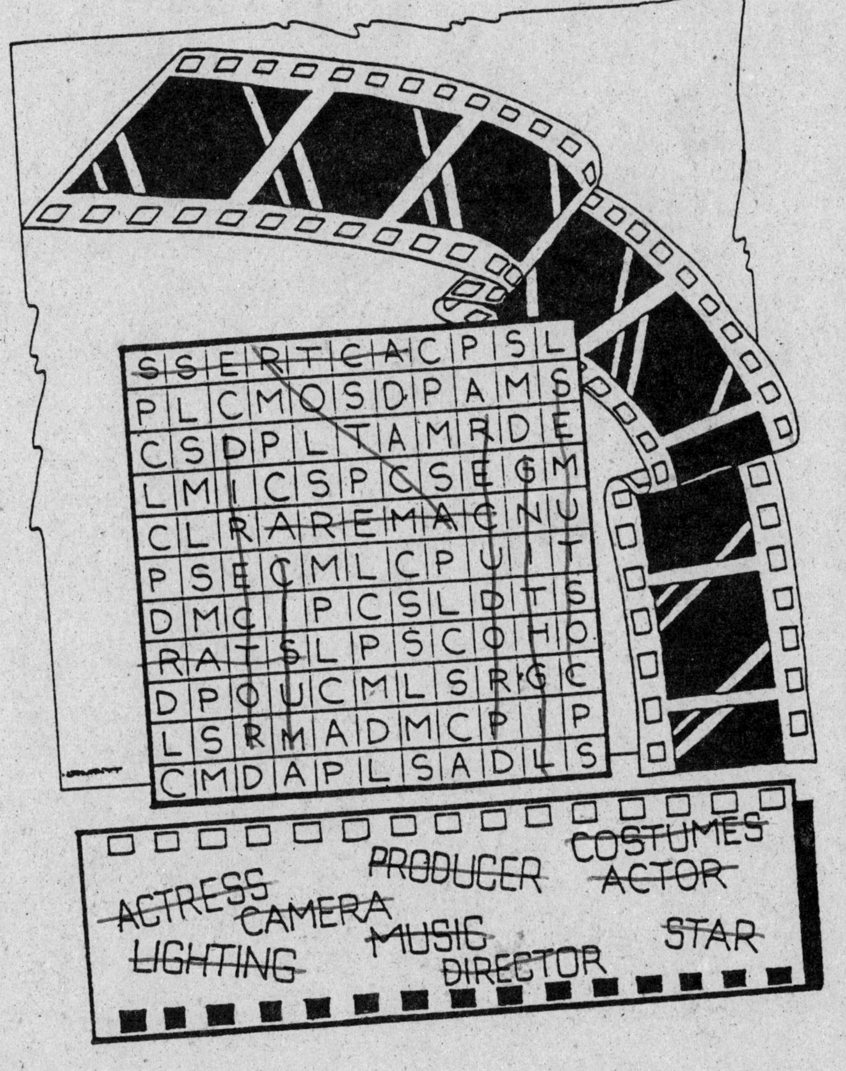

26

See if you can count the number of feathers in the picture.

27

See if you can pair the identical squares.

Join the dots from Nos. 1 – 45 to find a hidden picture.

28

29

See if you can pair the identical squares.

CAN YOU MATCH THE SPORTS PERSONALITIES TO THE CORRECT SPORT?

MOTOR RACING	FRANK BRUNO
TENNIS	STEVE DAVIS
RUGBY	IAN BOTHAM
CRICKET	JOHN BARNES
SNOOKER	NIGEL MANSELL
BOXING	STEFFI GRAF
FOOTBALL	WILL CARLING

31

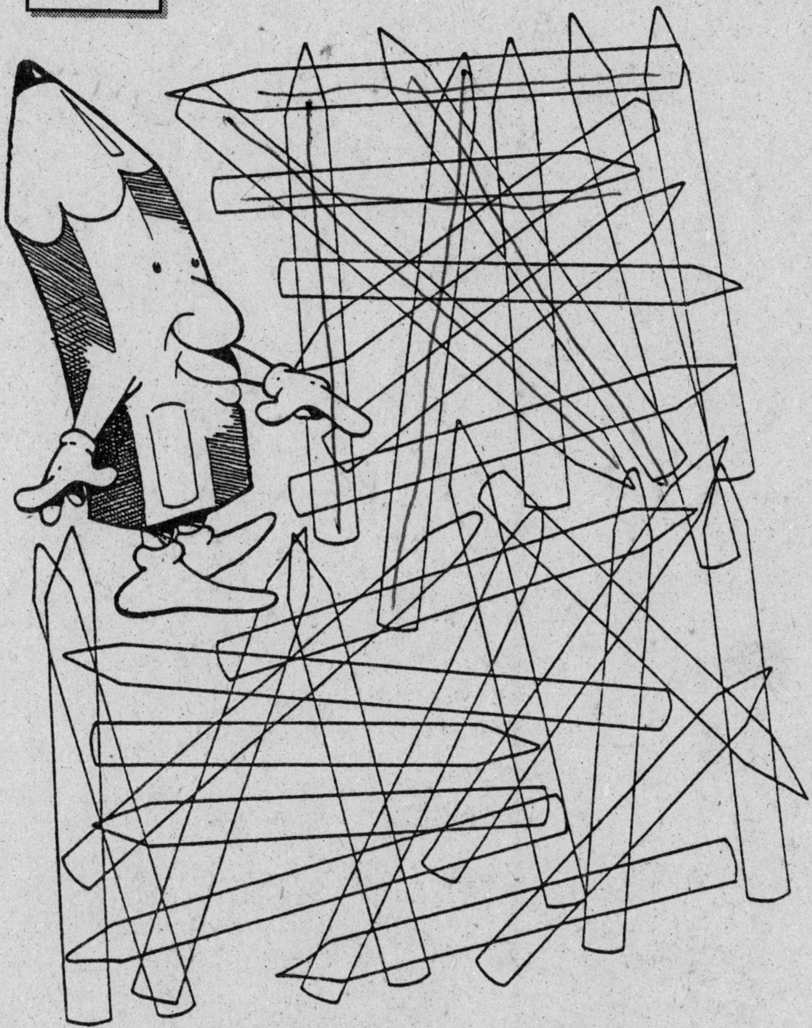

How many pencils are there in the picture?

32
MAKE
-A-WORD
RELBOURNO
1
2
3
4
5
6
7
8
9
9
TAKE THE FIRST LETTER OF EACH OF THE
OBJECTS IN THESE SQUARES AND MAKE
A NEW WORD.

33

Can you find six pairs of identical squares?

34

How many things can you find in this picture that start with the letter F? Circle all the things you can name.

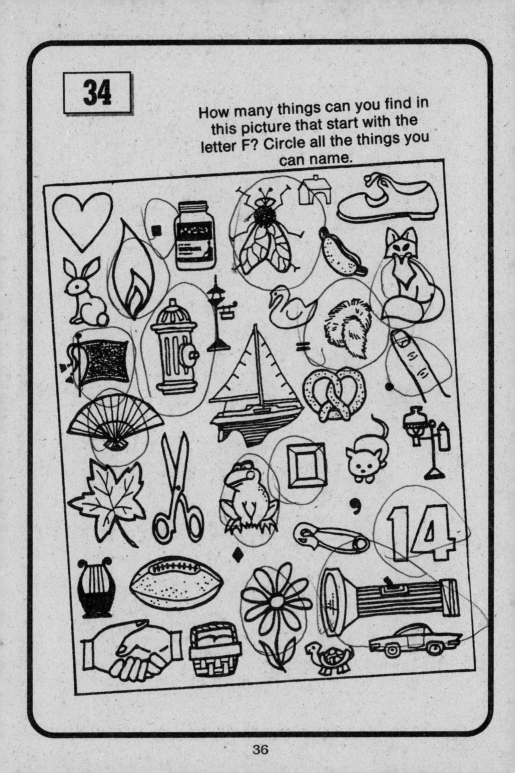

Spot the Differences

There are ten differences in the two pictures below. The left is the original.

35

36

See if you can complete the three drawings of the little gnome with her bowl of cake mixture.

37

Solve the arithmetic problem on the left and then find the answer to the problem hidden in the number on the right.

45 − 12	523334
60 + 21	816521
75 − 25	250701
11 + 202	215213
24 + 12	263612
48 − 13	43035
34 + 3	40937
17 + 15	37532
92 − 12	80710

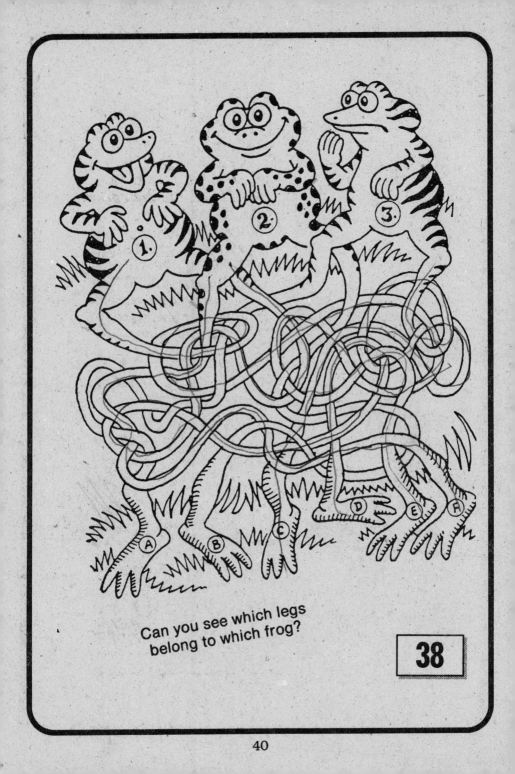

Can you see which legs belong to which frog?

38

39

Cut along the dotted line surrounding the two boxers. Glue this to the underside of a cardboard box lid. Now cut out the two 'boxing gloves' at the top then place them in the 'boxing ring'. You have now to get the two gloves in the circles at the ends of the wrists of the boxers by shaking the lid – gently. Both gloves must be in place at the same time. It's not easy.

40

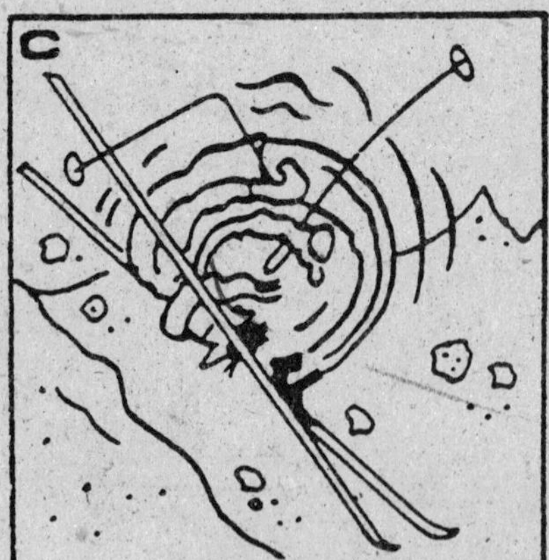

Can you place these pictures in correct order to tell a story?

41

Match the top half of the ship to the bottom half.

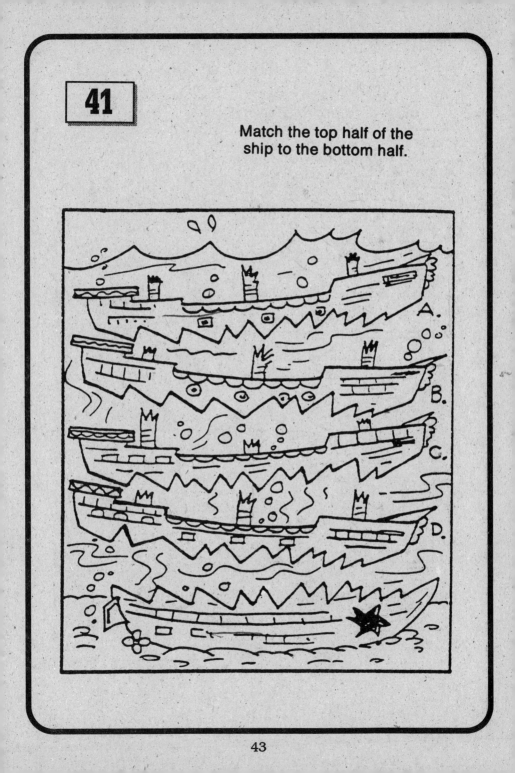

42

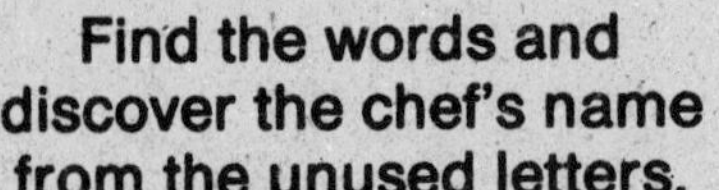

Find the words and discover the chef's name from the unused letters.

N	H	E	K	A	C	N	A	P
P	E	P	P	E	R	E	O	U
J	M	K	K	E	S	R	D	H
E	A	E	C	E	R	A	U	C
L	E	I	E	I	E	G	H	T
L	R	H	D	R	H	O	A	E
Y	C	G	B	O	P	C	M	K
R	E	G	R	U	B	M	A	H

BEST LONG GRAIN

DOUBLE DAIRY

FINEST SCOTS OATS

TOMATO SAUCE

CHEF'S NAME.

CAN YOU HELP ME TO REACH MY HOME ON THE LEAF IN THE FAR CORNER OF THE GARDEN?
A
B
C
D

43

44

Shade in the shapes to discover a hidden picture.

Complete the picture by drawing the top squares in their correct position below.

45

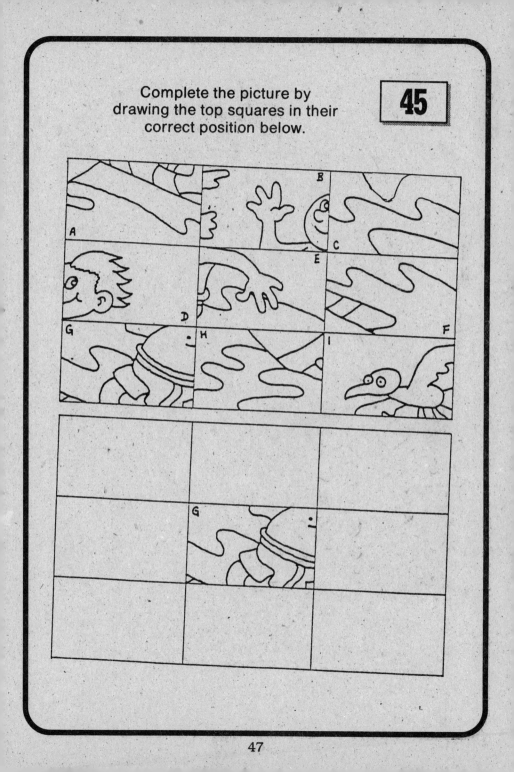

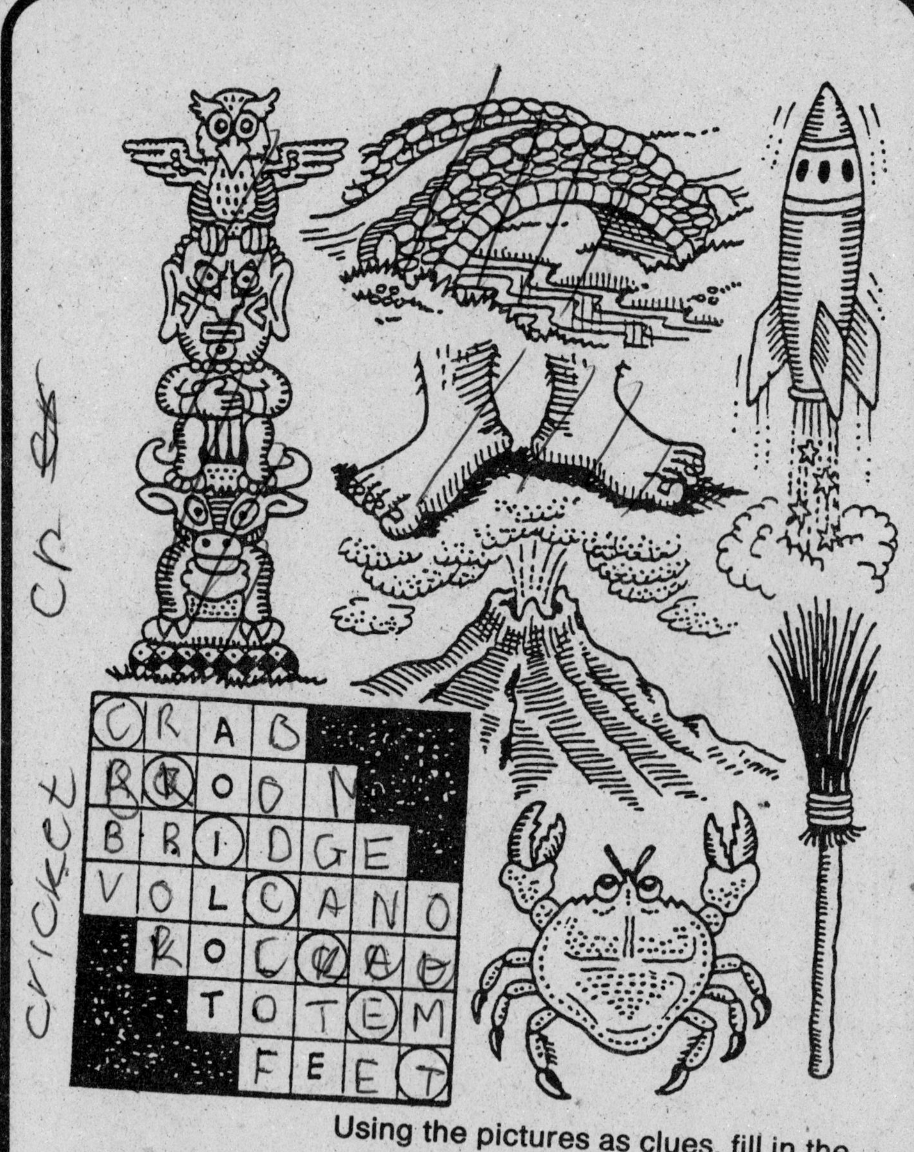

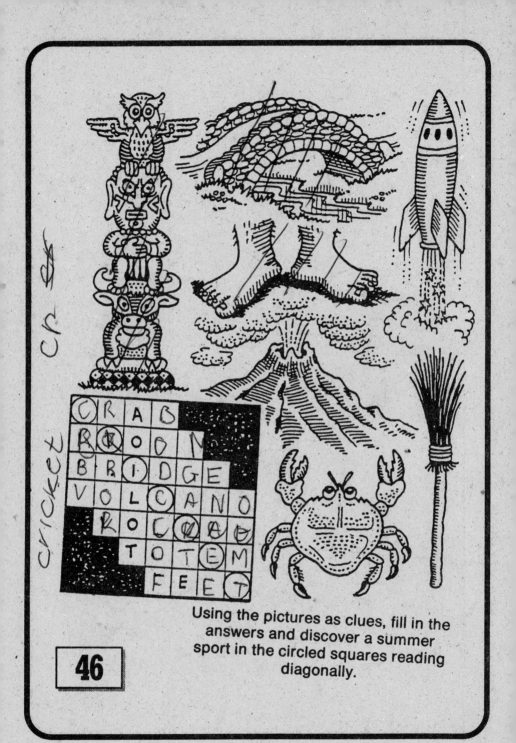

Using the pictures as clues, fill in the answers and discover a summer sport in the circled squares reading diagonally.

46

How many ovals are in the picture?

47

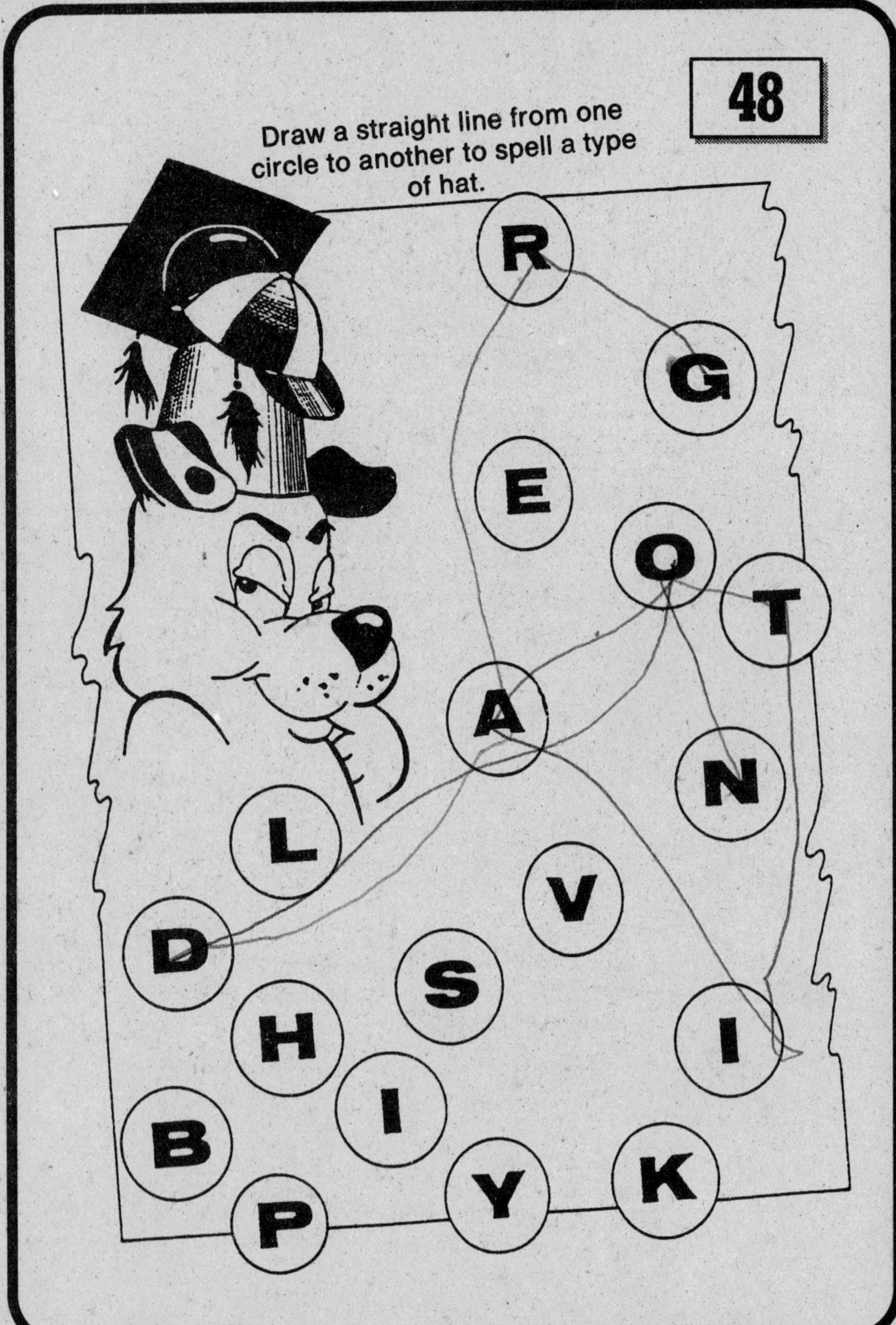
48
Draw a straight line from one circle to another to spell a type of hat.
R
G
E
O
T
A
N
L
V
D
S
H
I
B
I
K
Y
P

49

These three friends are out fishing. Which one has caught the fish?

50

How many bubbles can you see?

51

Buried Treasure!

Write down the first letter of each place you come to when marking the map. These letters spell out what the treasure is.

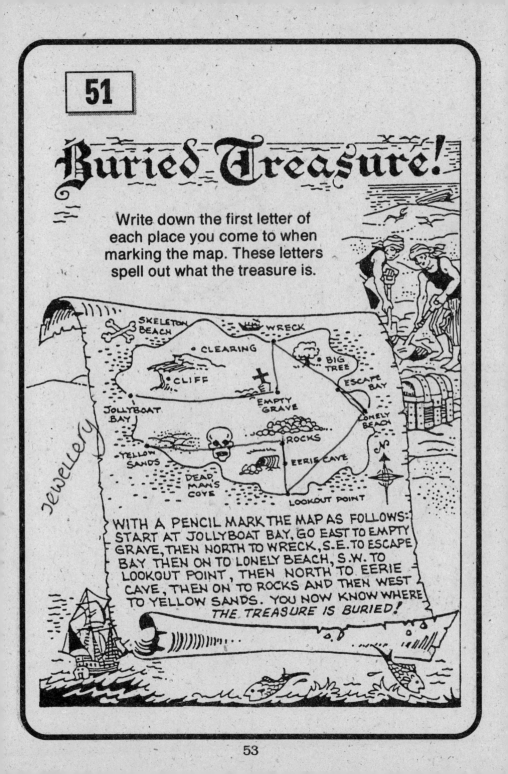

SKELETON BEACH
WRECK
CLEARING
BIG TREE
CLIFF
ESCAPE BAY
EMPTY GRAVE
JOLLYBOAT BAY
LONELY BEACH
ROCKS
YELLOW SANDS
EERIE CAVE
DEAD MAN'S COVE
LOOKOUT POINT

WITH A PENCIL MARK THE MAP AS FOLLOWS: START AT JOLLYBOAT BAY, GO EAST TO EMPTY GRAVE, THEN NORTH TO WRECK, S.E. TO ESCAPE BAY THEN ON TO LONELY BEACH, S.W. TO LOOKOUT POINT, THEN NORTH TO EERIE CAVE, THEN ON TO ROCKS AND THEN WEST TO YELLOW SANDS. YOU NOW KNOW WHERE *THE TREASURE IS BURIED!*

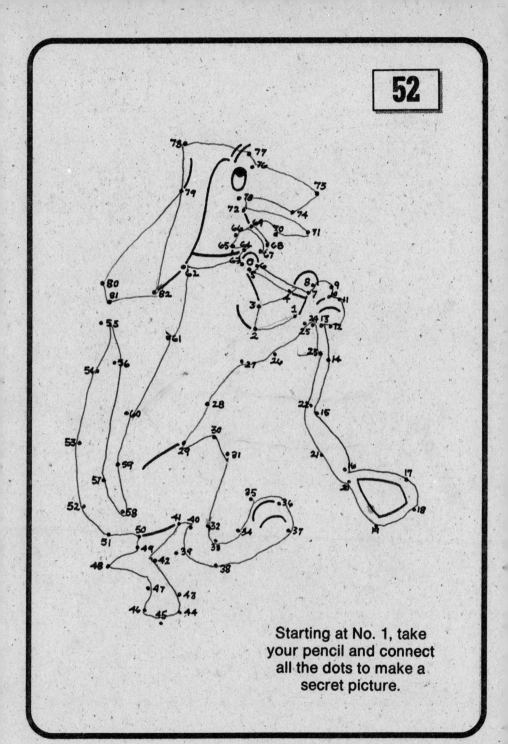

52

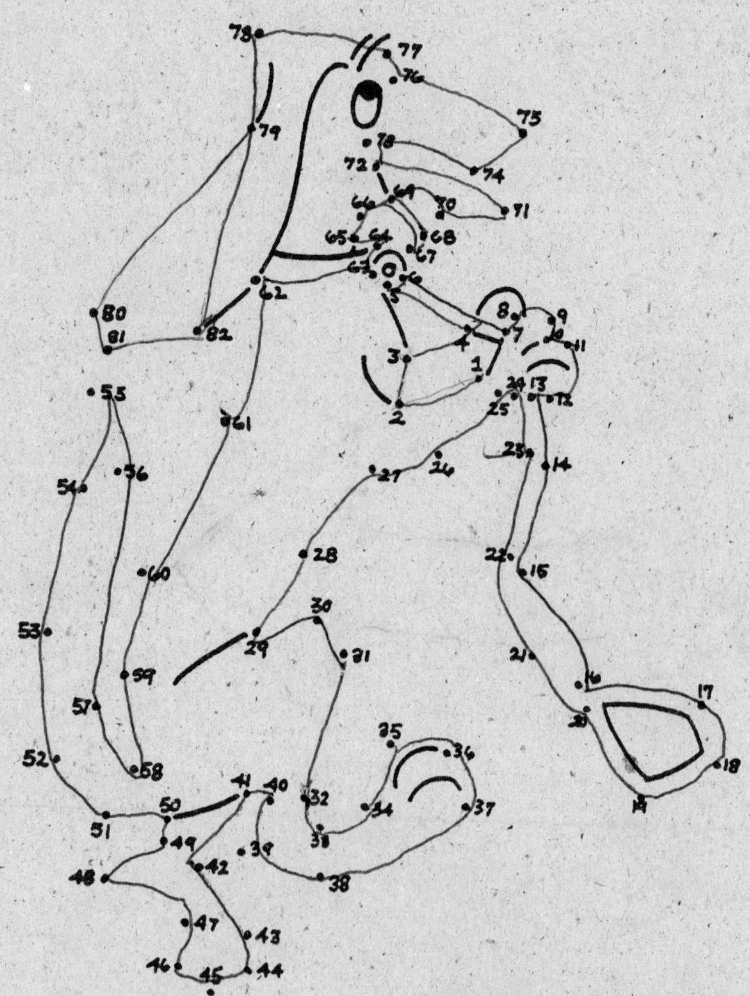

Starting at No. 1, take your pencil and connect all the dots to make a secret picture.

53

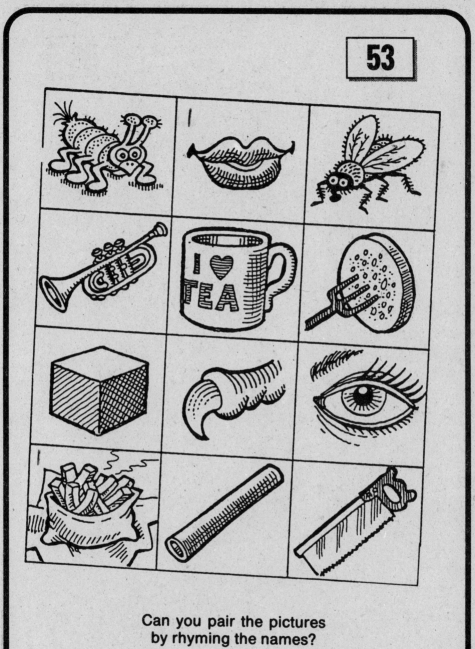

Can you pair the pictures by rhyming the names?

54

There are ten differences between the two pictures. Can you spot them?

MONSTER MAZE

55

WATCH OUT FOR THE MONSTERS ON THE WAY TO THE CASTLE.

56
1
3
5
6
2
7
4
8
Which two pigs are the same as the large drawing?

57
Find the continuous black line from wasp to ice cream.

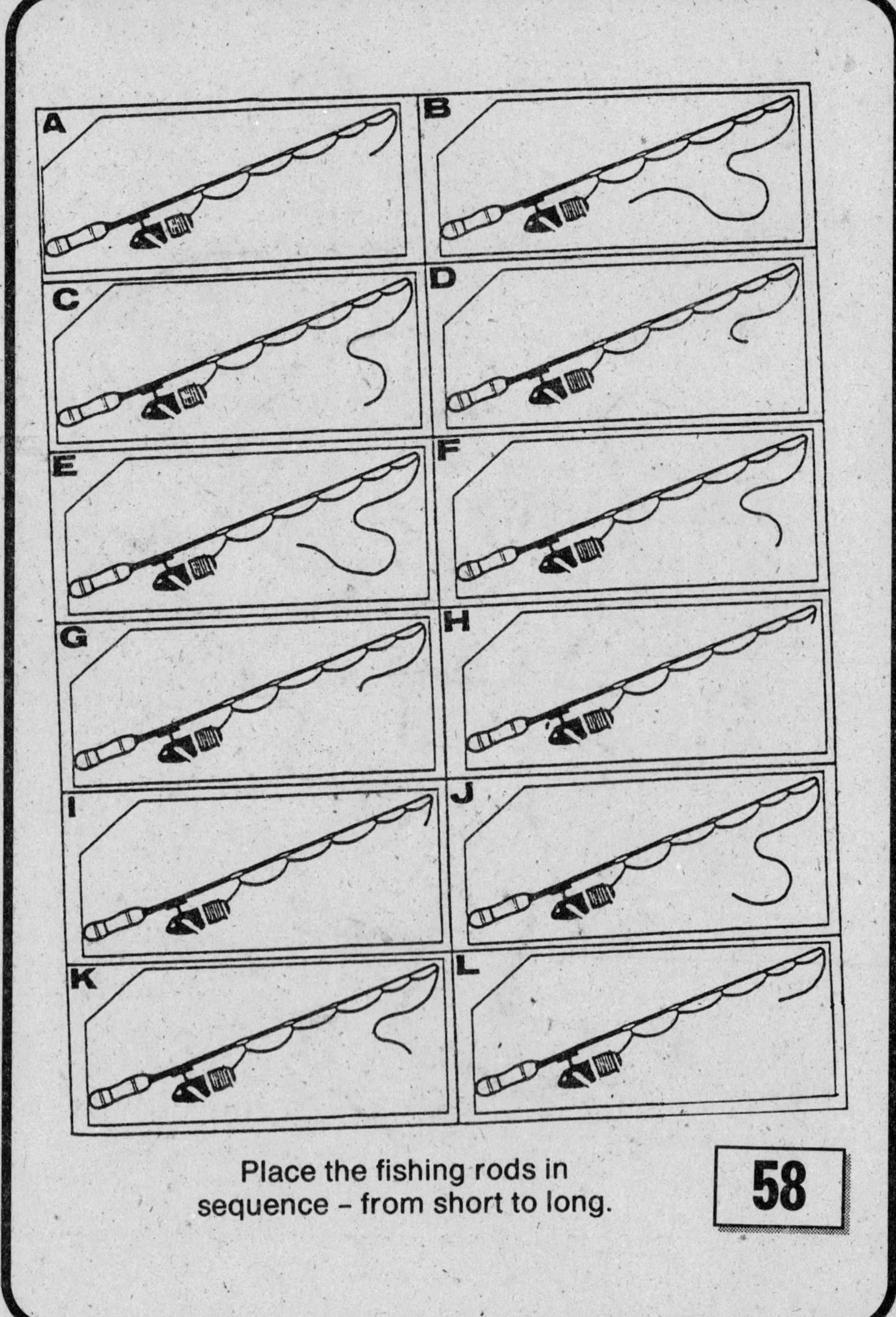

Place the fishing rods in sequence – from short to long.

59

Superintendent Smith, during a meeting, is searching for somebody who has swindled a lady. He knows for sure that the person in question:

- is in perfectly good health.
- doesn't wear rubber footwear.
- hasn't brought a hat.
- doesn't like reading.
- hates being seated.

Can you help the superintendent?

Can you place the two halves
together to make complete circles?
60
1
2
3
4
5
6
7
8

61

Can you spot ten differences between the two pictures?

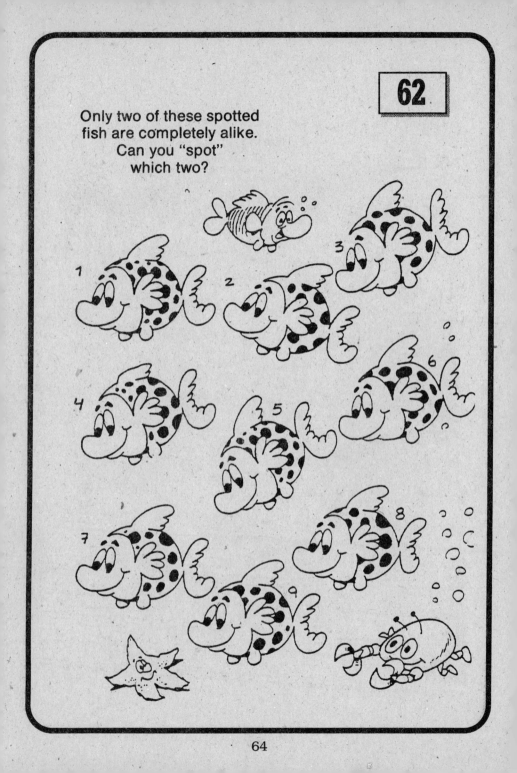

Only two of these spotted fish are completely alike. Can you "spot" which two?

63

Can you decode the secret message?

HGZIGRMT UILN GSV
SLFHV, DZOP GL
GSV XILHHILZWH ZMW
GFIM OVUG ULOOLD
GSV ILZW GLDZIWH
GSV GSIVV GIVVH.
GSV GIVZHFIV
RH YFIRVW FMWVI
GSV OZITV HGLMV
LKKLHRGV.
15
Z Y X W V U T S R Q P O N
A B C D E F G H I J K L M
M L K J I H G F E D C B A
N O P Q R S T U V W X Y Z

64

Shade in the shapes that contain a dot to discover a hidden picture.

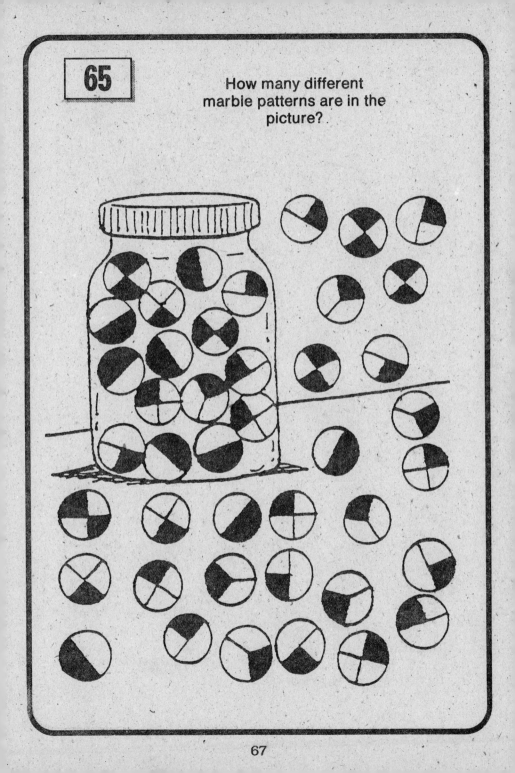

65

How many different marble patterns are in the picture?

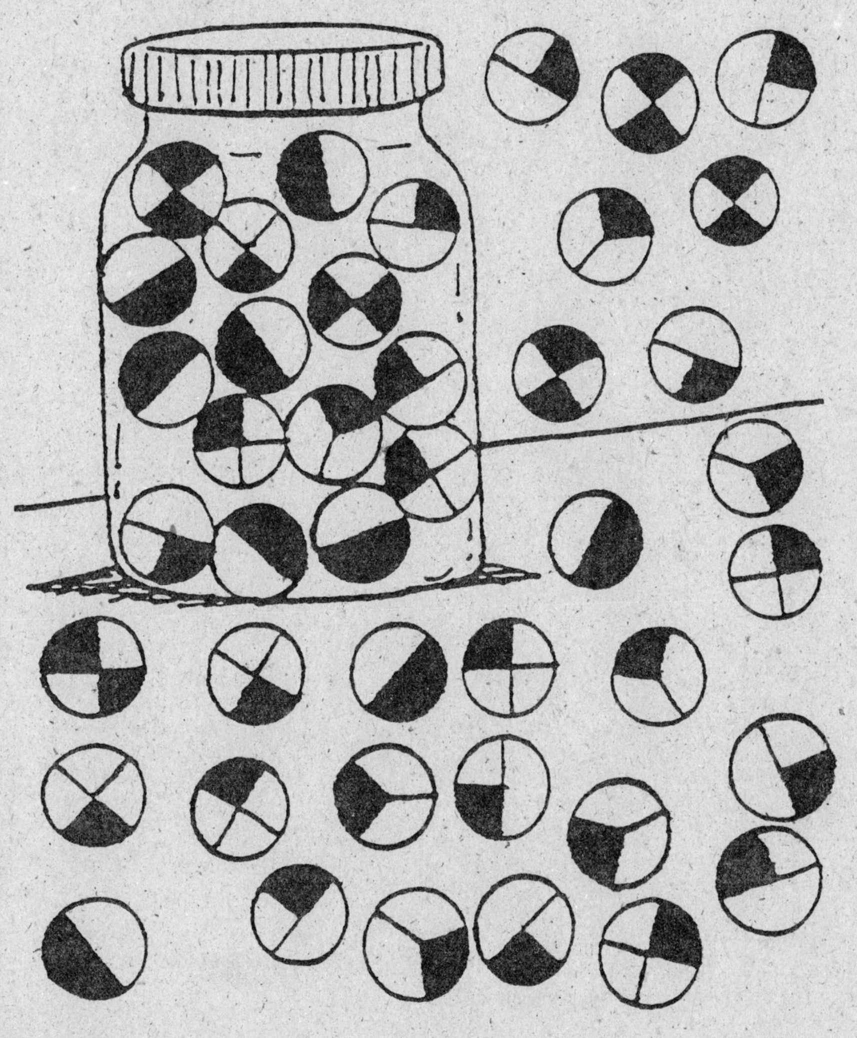

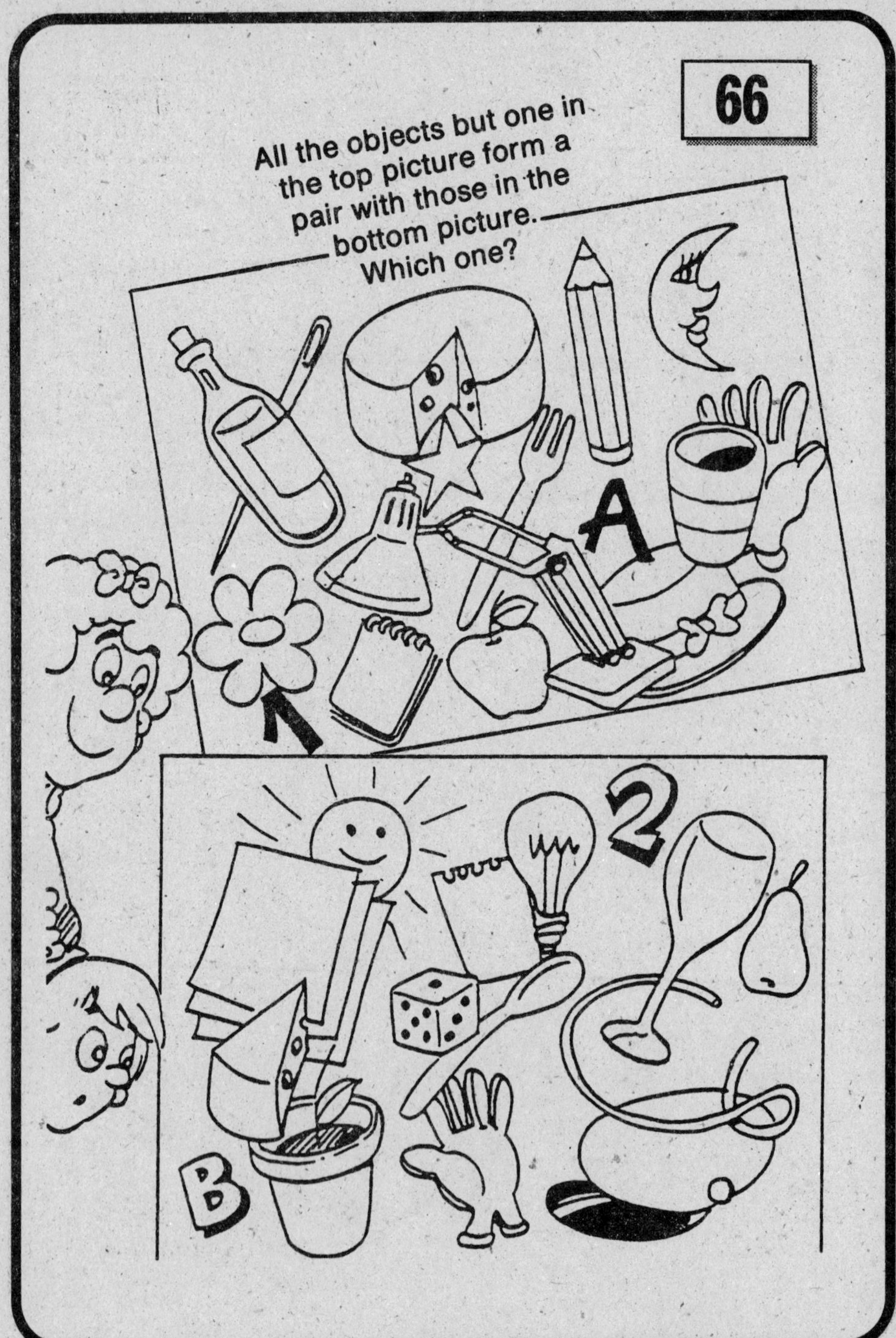
66
All the objects but one in the top picture form a pair with those in the bottom picture. Which one?
A
2
B

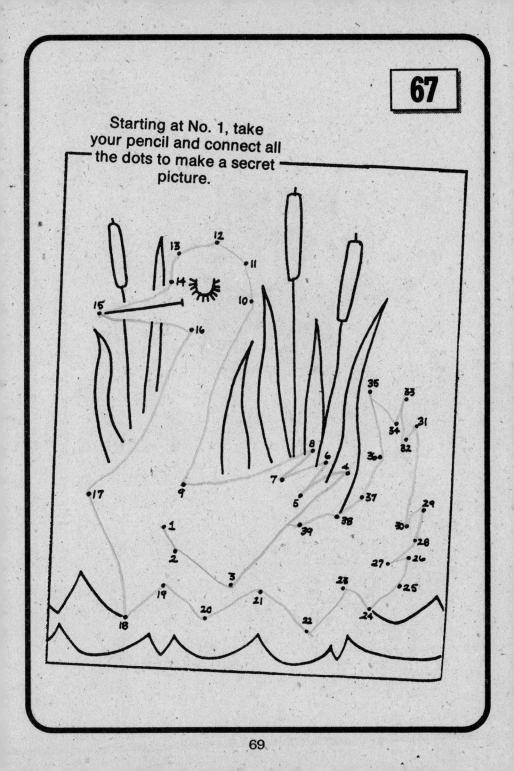

Starting at No. 1, take your pencil and connect all the dots to make a secret picture.

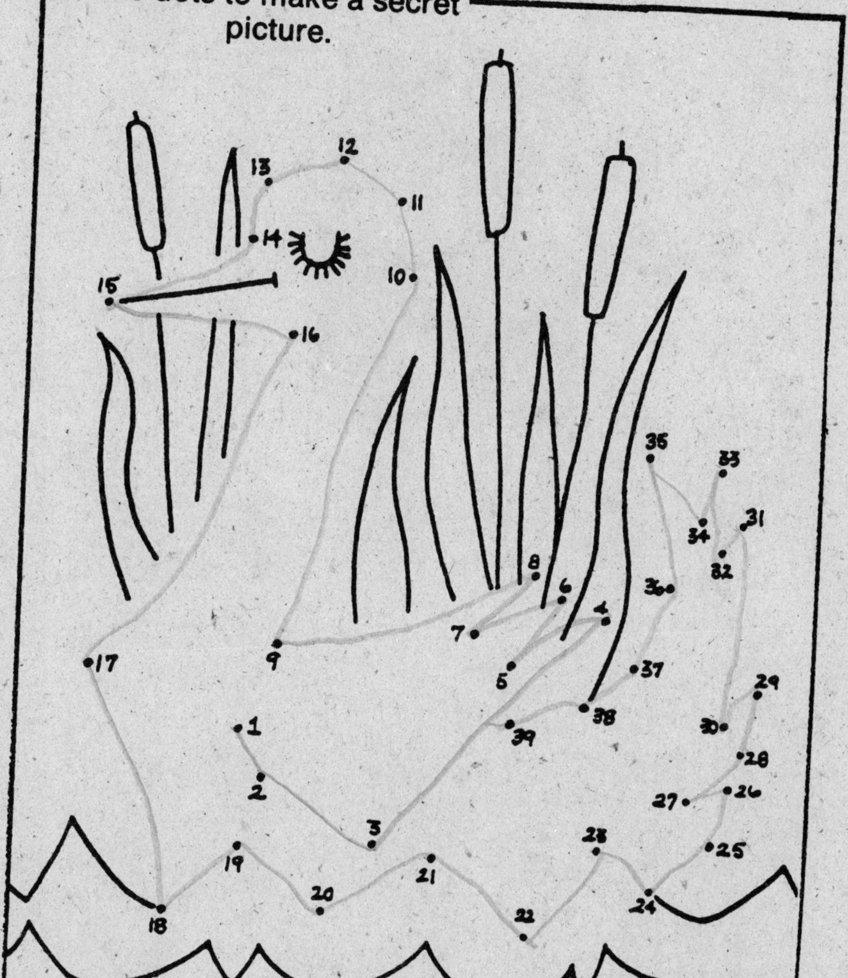

68

Which line will equal the blackboard's sum?

69
A
B
C
Which shadow matches the dog?

70

The first word of this proverb is in one style of lettering, and the second in another and so on, with six words in all. Can you sort it out?

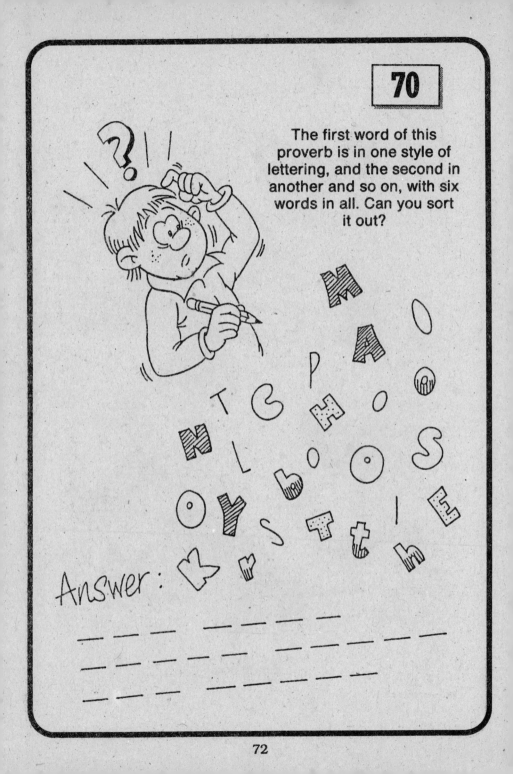

71

Fill in only the△triangles and you will see a hidden picture.

72

Can you spot ten differences between the two pictures?

73

KNOW YOUR WEATHER

Using the pictures on the left as clues, fill in the missing words. The picture shows different types of weather conditions.

MESSAGES
BEEP
BEEP
BEEP
BEEP
74
PLEASE HELP ME FIND THE WAY TO MY DE-CODING MACHINE. THERE IS A JUMBLED MESSAGE FOR YOU TO UNWIND, USING THE CODE BELOW, IN NUMBERS.
A
B
C
D
BEEEP
32. 51. 23. 23. 53.

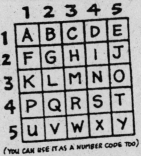

You'll find a communication code on the right. Copy the code, and give a copy to a friend.

When you want to send a message, tap out the numbers. Across first and then down. e.g..... G would be 2 taps (a break) 2 taps.

	1	2	3	4	5
1	A	B	C	D	E
2	F	G	H	I	J
3	K	L	M	N	O
4	P	Q	R	S	T
5	U	V	W	X	Y

(YOU CAN USE IT AS A NUMBER CODE TOO)

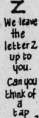

Z
We leave the letter Z up to you.
Can you think of a tap for it?

75

One of these characters is wearing two objects that belong to one of the other characters.

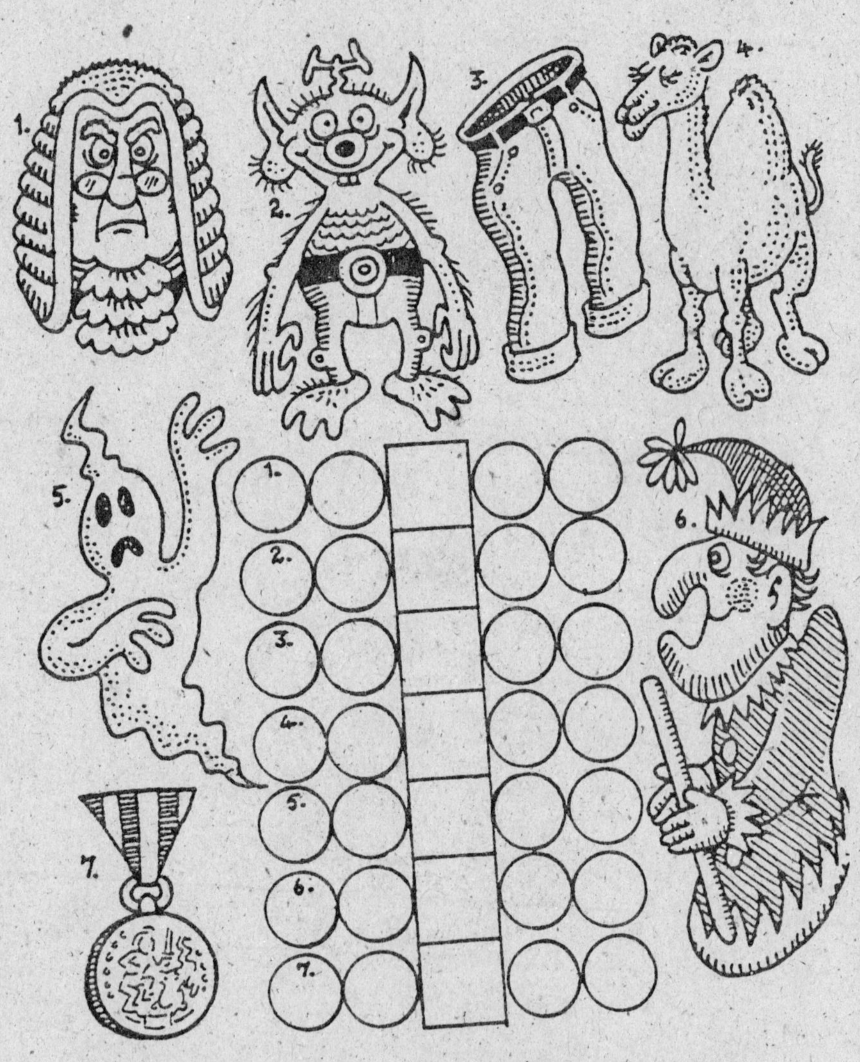

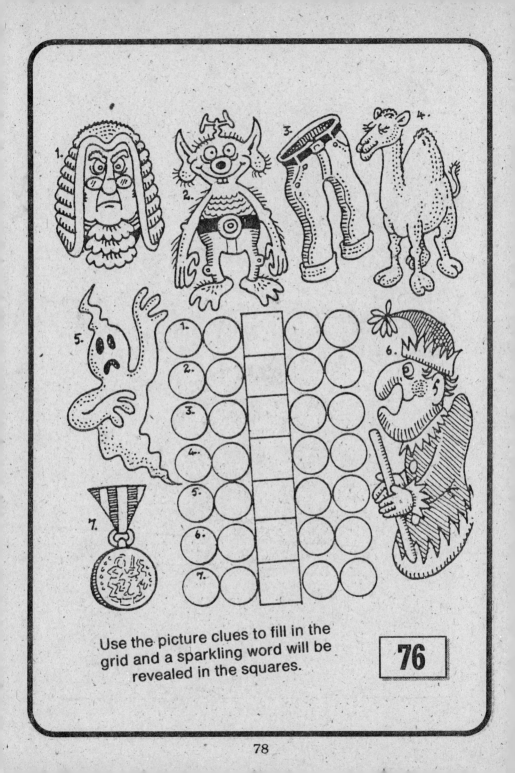

Use the picture clues to fill in the grid and a sparkling word will be revealed in the squares.

76

77

Which arrow will strike the bullseye?

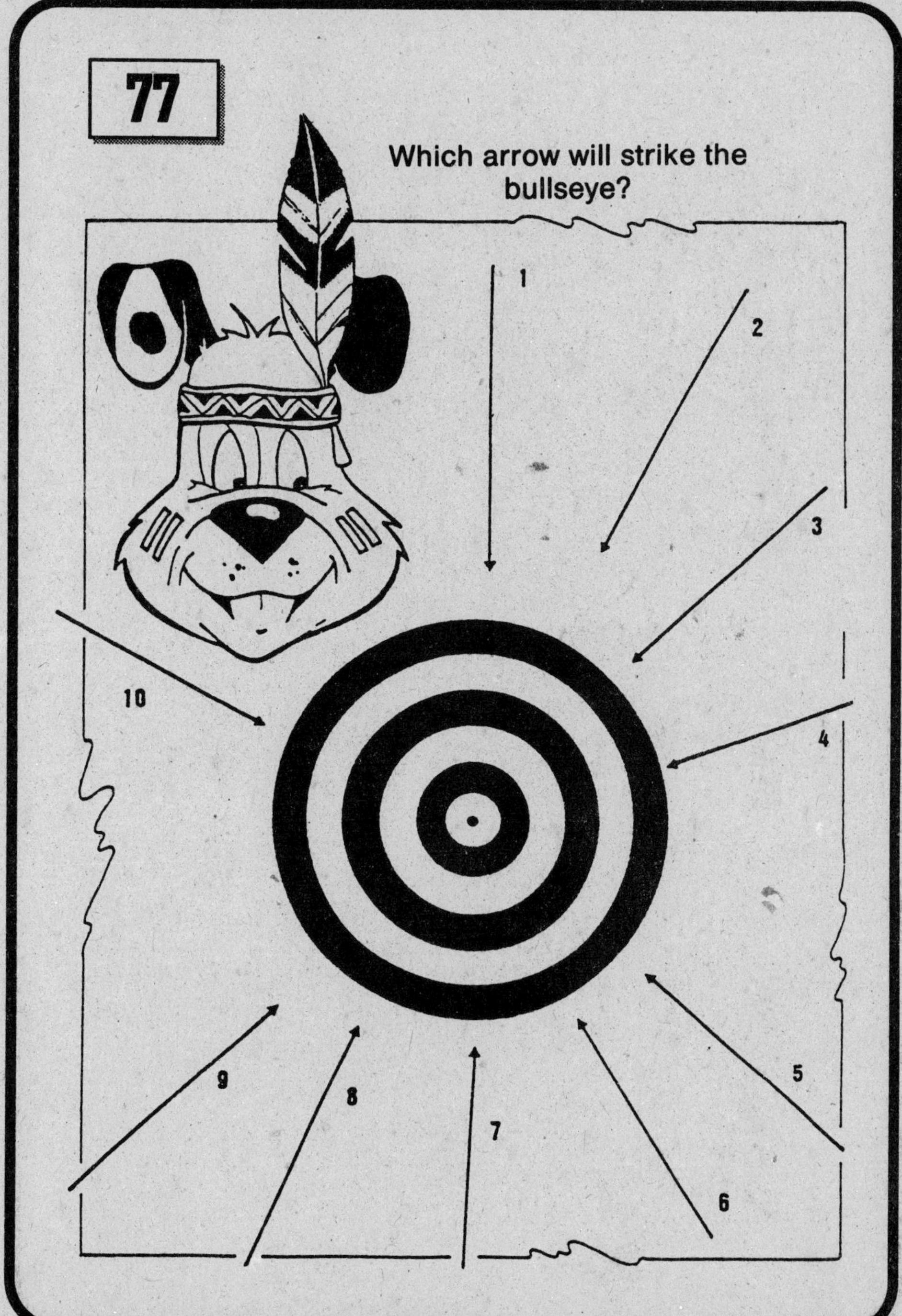

78

A PICTURE TO PAINT!

79

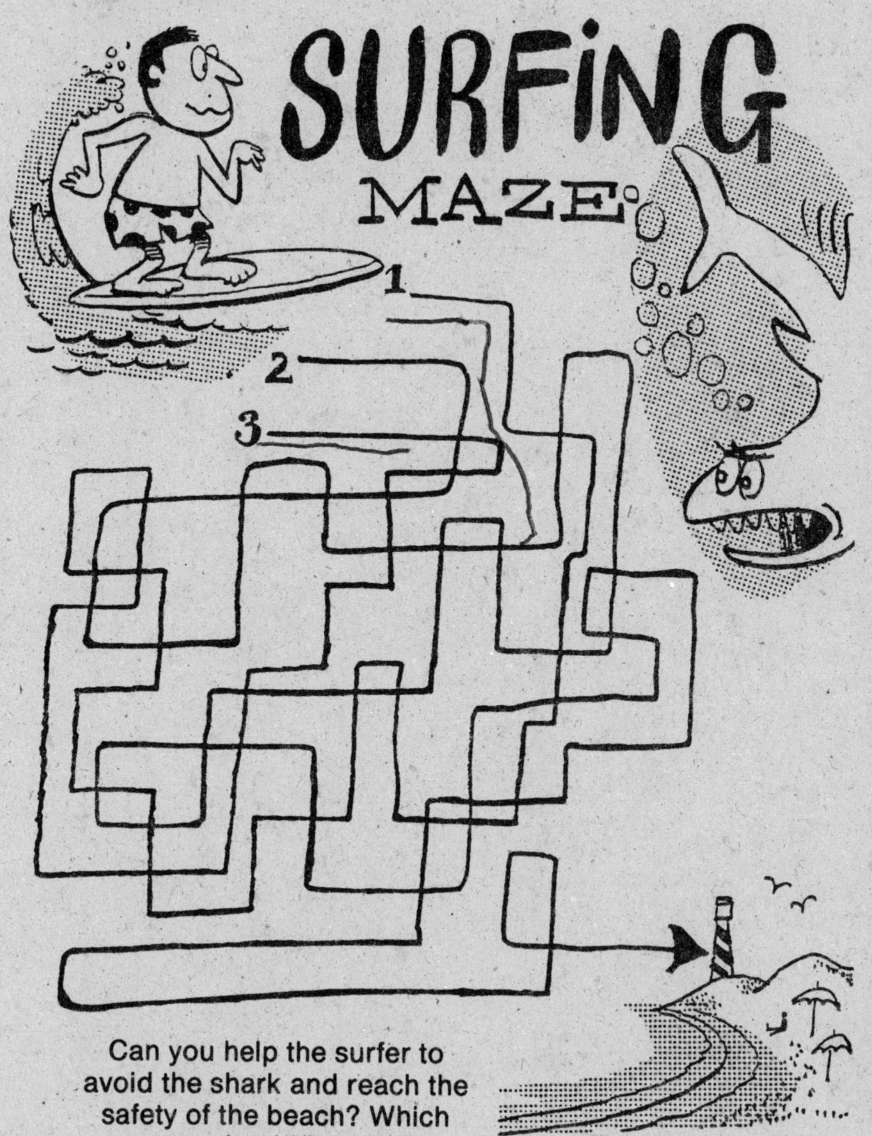

Can you help the surfer to avoid the shark and reach the safety of the beach? Which route should he take?

80

Director's Dilemma

I'M IN A REAL FIX. I CAN'T FIND MY WAY TO THE STAGE. CAN YOU HELP ME? WHAT WILL I FIND WHEN I GET THERE?

· JOIN THE DOTS.

81

How many shoes has the shoe mender repaired?

82

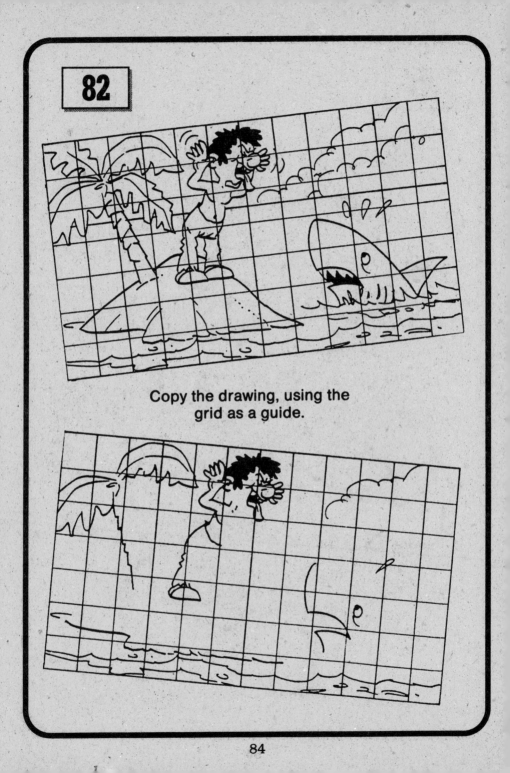

Copy the drawing, using the grid as a guide.

83

The Unhappy Bookworm

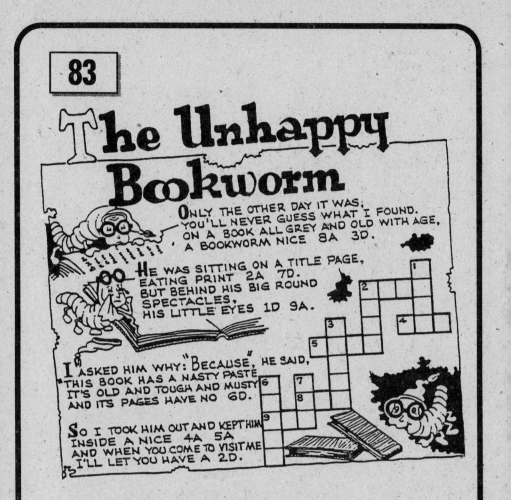

ONLY THE OTHER DAY IT WAS;
YOU'LL NEVER GUESS WHAT I FOUND.
ON A BOOK ALL GREY AND OLD WITH AGE,
A BOOKWORM NICE 8A 3D.

HE WAS SITTING ON A TITLE PAGE,
EATING PRINT 2A 7D.
BUT BEHIND HIS BIG ROUND
SPECTACLES,
HIS LITTLE EYES 1D 9A.

I ASKED HIM WHY: "BECAUSE", HE SAID,
"THIS BOOK HAS A NASTY PASTE
IT'S OLD AND TOUGH AND MUSTY
AND ITS PAGES HAVE NO 6D.

SO I TOOK HIM OUT AND KEPT HIM
INSIDE A NICE 4A 5A
AND WHEN YOU COME TO VISIT ME
I'LL LET YOU HAVE A 2D.

Some words have been left out of this story of the unhappy bookworm. See if you can work out what they are and use them to complete the crossword. If you do this correctly, you will find that it has a happy ending.

1	2	3	4	5	6	7	8	9	10	11	12	13	14	15	16
A	B	C	D	E	F	G	H	I	J	K	L	M	N	O	P

17	18	19	20	21	22	23	24	25	26
Q	R	S	T	U	V	W	X	Y	Z

WHAT DO YOU CALL A 2.15.15.13.5.18.1.14.7 THAT WON'T COME BACK, BRUCE?
A 19.20.9.3.11!!
84

85

Which lock will the key fit?

86

From the BUILDER'S bag

Here's an easy crossword. Just complete it by filling in the names of all the objects we have pictured.

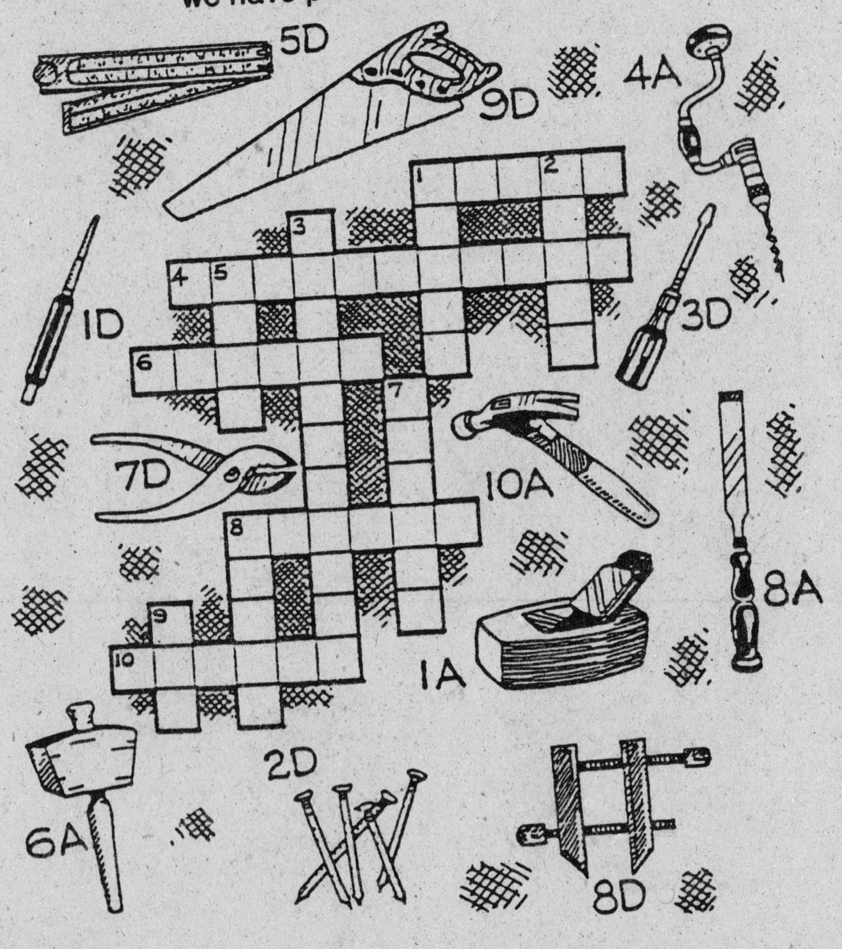

87

Colour in only the boxes that contain the letters D A C H S H U N D and you'll find a trick (another name for dachshund) and treat (something to eat).

88

Can you find the two that are exactly alike? Only two are.

89

Find the unbroken line from one lamb's tail to the other.

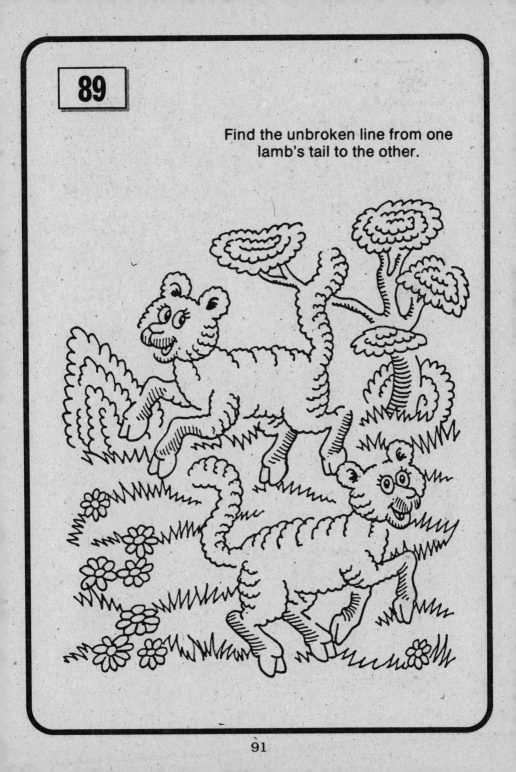

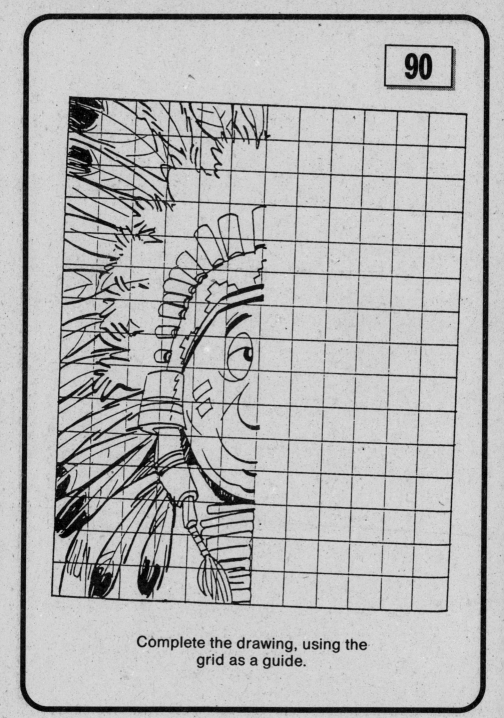

90

Complete the drawing, using the grid as a guide.

91

Complete the picture by drawing the above squares in their correct position below.

92

Shade the shapes which contain 1 spot and 3 spots to discover a hidden picture.

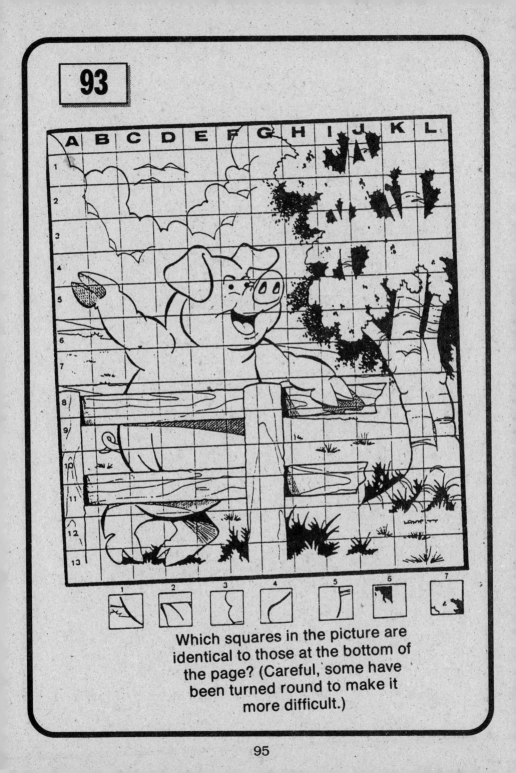

93

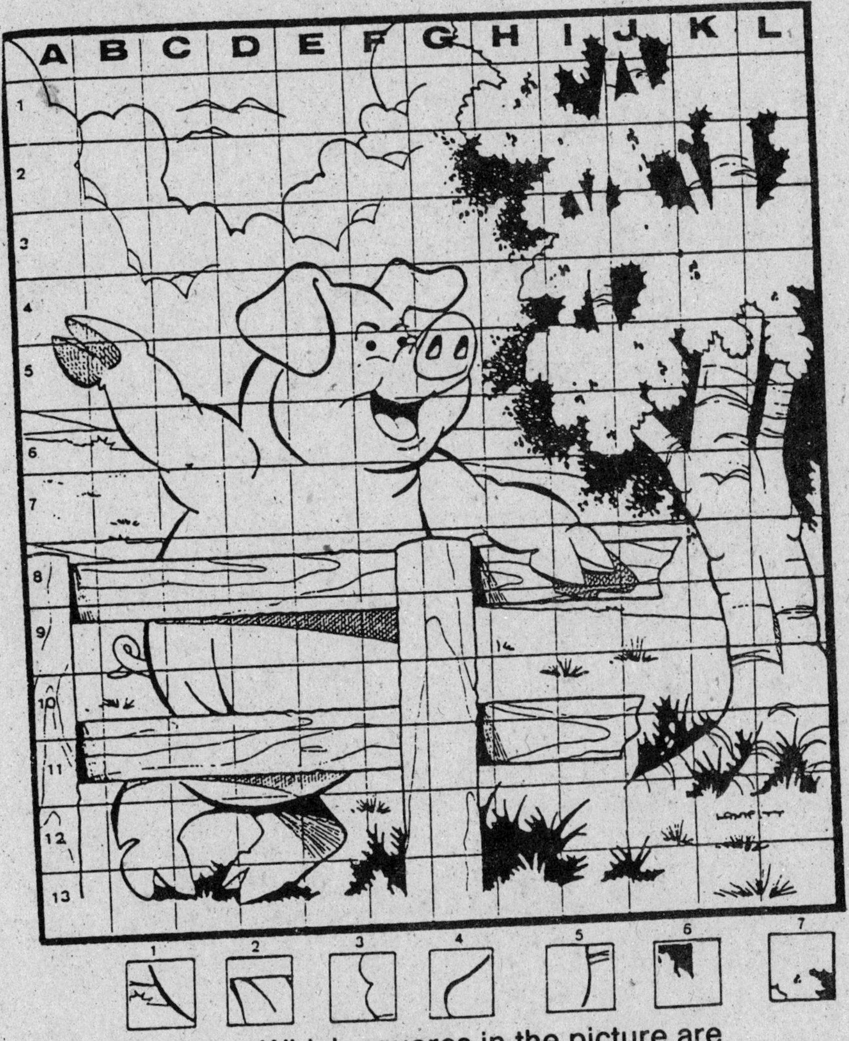

Which squares in the picture are identical to those at the bottom of the page? (Careful, some have been turned round to make it more difficult.)

94

Can you spot ten differences between the two pictures?

95

Can you pair the boats?

96

Put the first letter of each picture in the box to form a summer treat.

97

Solve the arithmetic problem on the left and then find the answer to the problem hidden in the number on the right.

10 + 20	210302
25 - 22	563010
64 + 36	638100
71 - 20	275131
83 + 21	810421
62 - 52	565210
49 + 6	55943
17 + 17	77342
13 - 6	37924

98

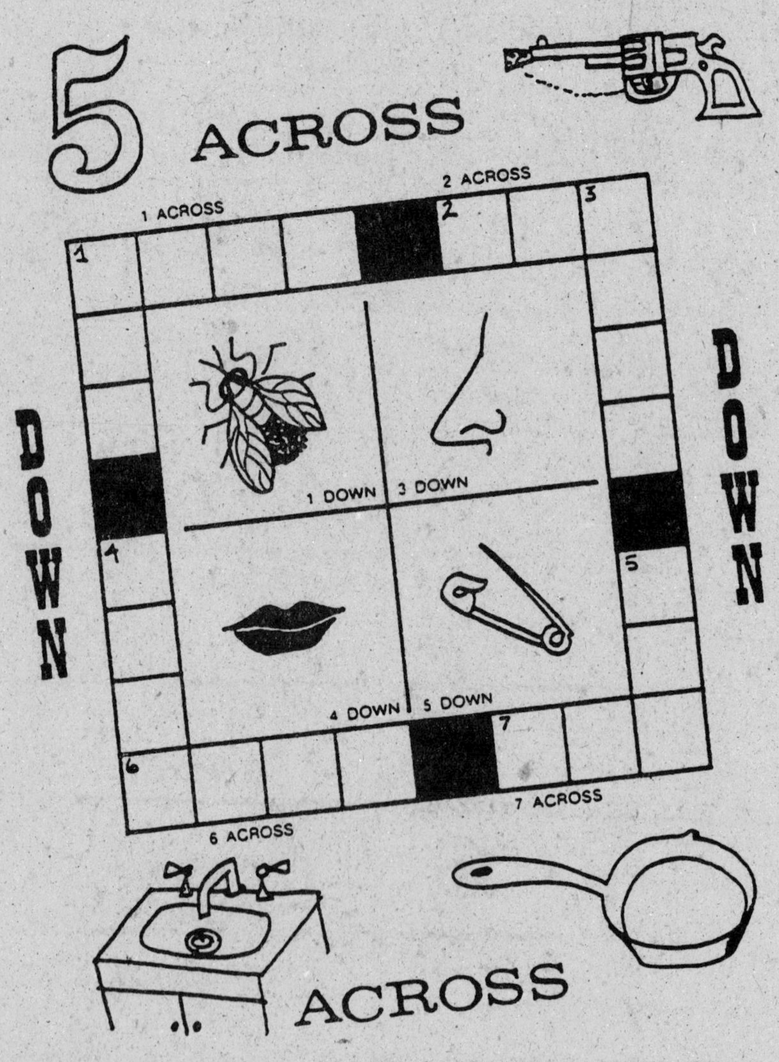
5 ACROSS
1 ACROSS
2 ACROSS
DOWN
DOWN
1 DOWN
3 DOWN
4 DOWN
5 DOWN
6 ACROSS
7 ACROSS
ACROSS

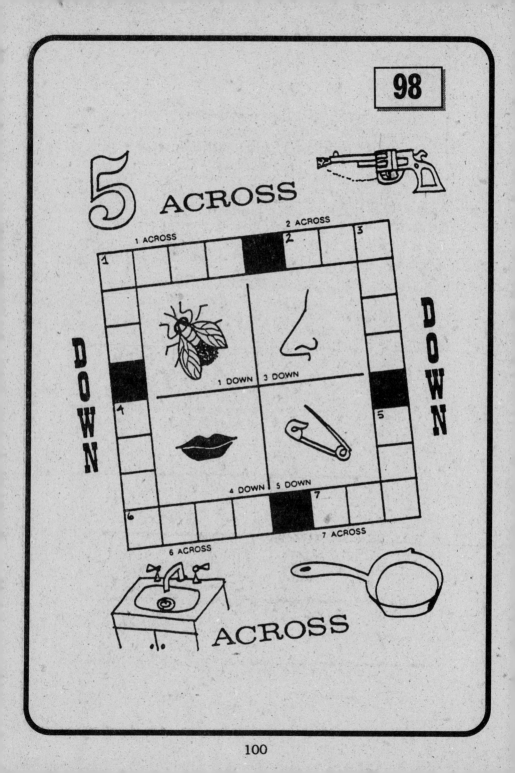

99

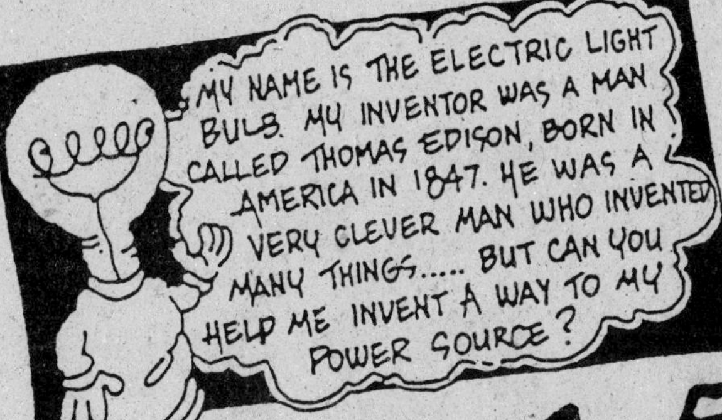

1. 2. 3. 4. 5.

ON

OFF

100

All arrows are about to reach the centre of the target, but two. Which two?

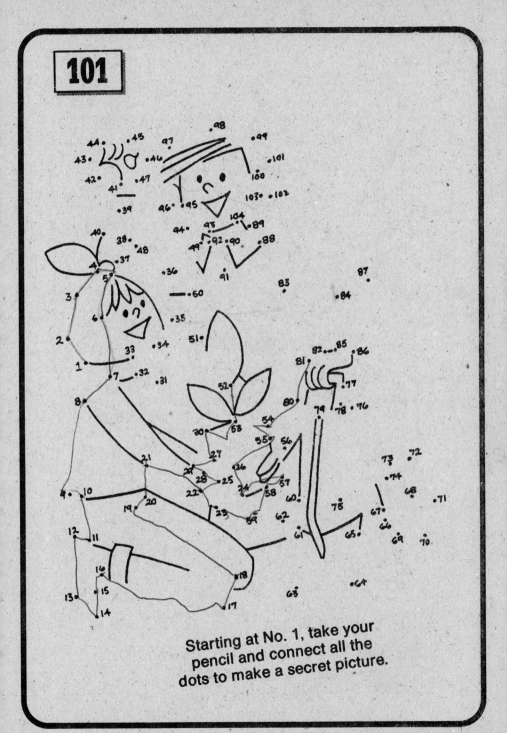

101

Starting at No. 1, take your pencil and connect all the dots to make a secret picture.

102

Here's a maze puzzle. All you have to do is take your pencil and draw a line from start to finish without crossing any black lines.

103

Can you find your way through the flower maze?

104

PLEASE....
HELP ME TO FIND
MY MISSING
TOOTH. FOLLOW
THE TRAIL FOR
ME.
1
2
3
4

105

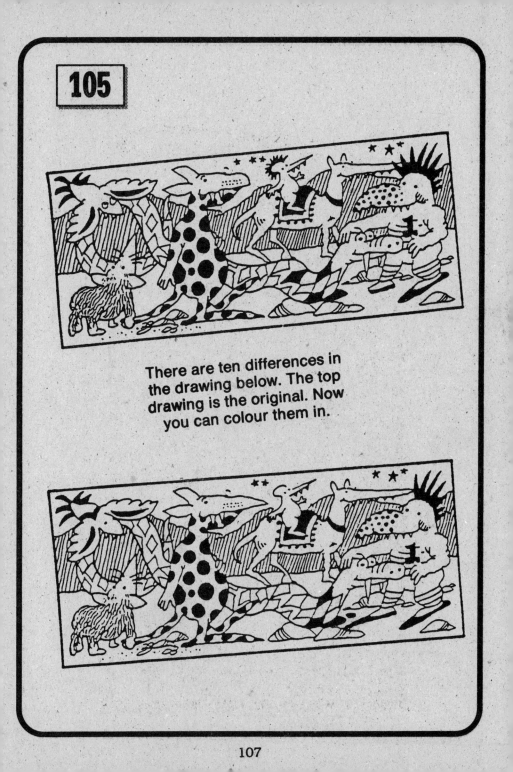

There are ten differences in the drawing below. The top drawing is the original. Now you can colour them in.

106

Which pieces do not come from the statue?

107

Shade the shapes with the odd numbers of dots.

108

109

Can you complete the rabbit's face?

110

The lower picture is an exact reflection of the top picture, but for 7 details. Which ones?

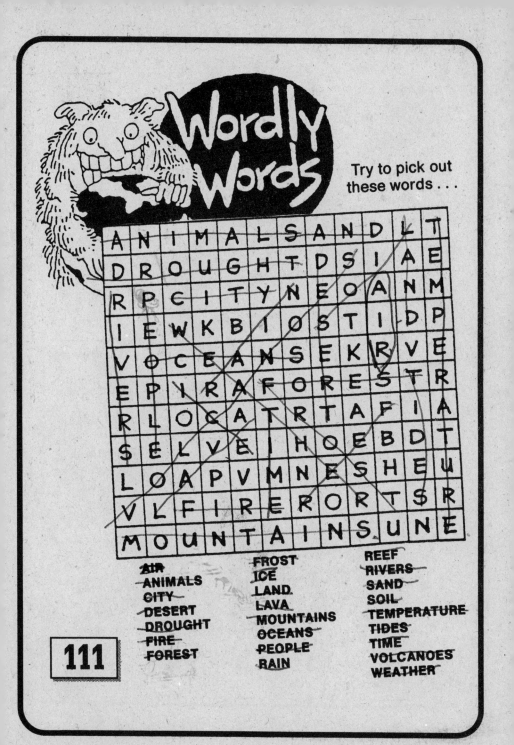

Try to pick out these words . . .

A	N	I	M	A	L	S	A	N	D	L	T
D	R	O	U	G	H	T	D	S	I	A	E
R	P	C	I	T	Y	N	E	O	A	N	M
I	E	W	K	B	I	O	S	T	I	D	P
V	O	C	E	A	N	S	E	K	R	V	E
E	P	I	R	A	F	O	R	E	S	T	R
R	L	O	C	A	T	R	T	A	F	I	A
S	E	L	V	E	I	H	O	E	B	D	T
L	O	A	P	V	M	N	E	S	H	E	U
V	L	F	I	R	E	R	O	R	T	S	R
M	O	U	N	T	A	I	N	S	U	N	E

AIR
ANIMALS
CITY
DESERT
DROUGHT
FIRE
FOREST
FROST
ICE
LAND
LAVA
MOUNTAINS
OCEANS
PEOPLE
RAIN
REEF
RIVERS
SAND
SOIL
TEMPERATURE
TIDES
TIME
VOLCANOES
WEATHER

111

112

Can you work out what is next in the sequence?

113

Find the missing letters and re-arrange them to spell something in the picture.

114
Can you find the two
that are exactly alike?
Two are.

115

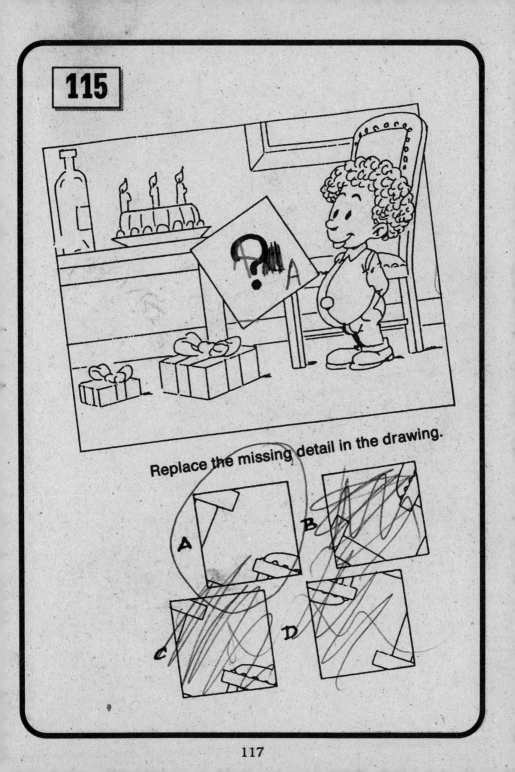

Replace the missing detail in the drawing.

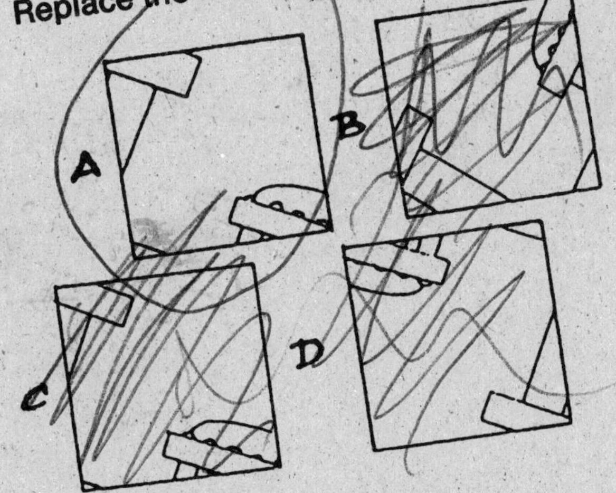

Here's a maze puzzle. All you have to do is take your pencil and draw a line from start to finish without crossing any black lines.

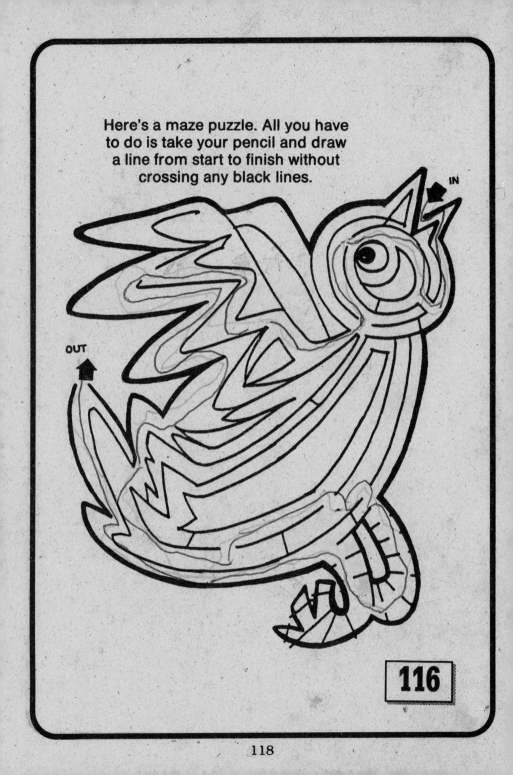

117

A picture for you to colour.

118

By studying the bubbles can you put the pictures in the correct order our artist has drawn them?

To find the mystery name below take the first letter of the first picture, the second of the second, etc. etc.

119

COLOUR-IN
120

121

Re-arrange the letters below, to form four words related with school

122

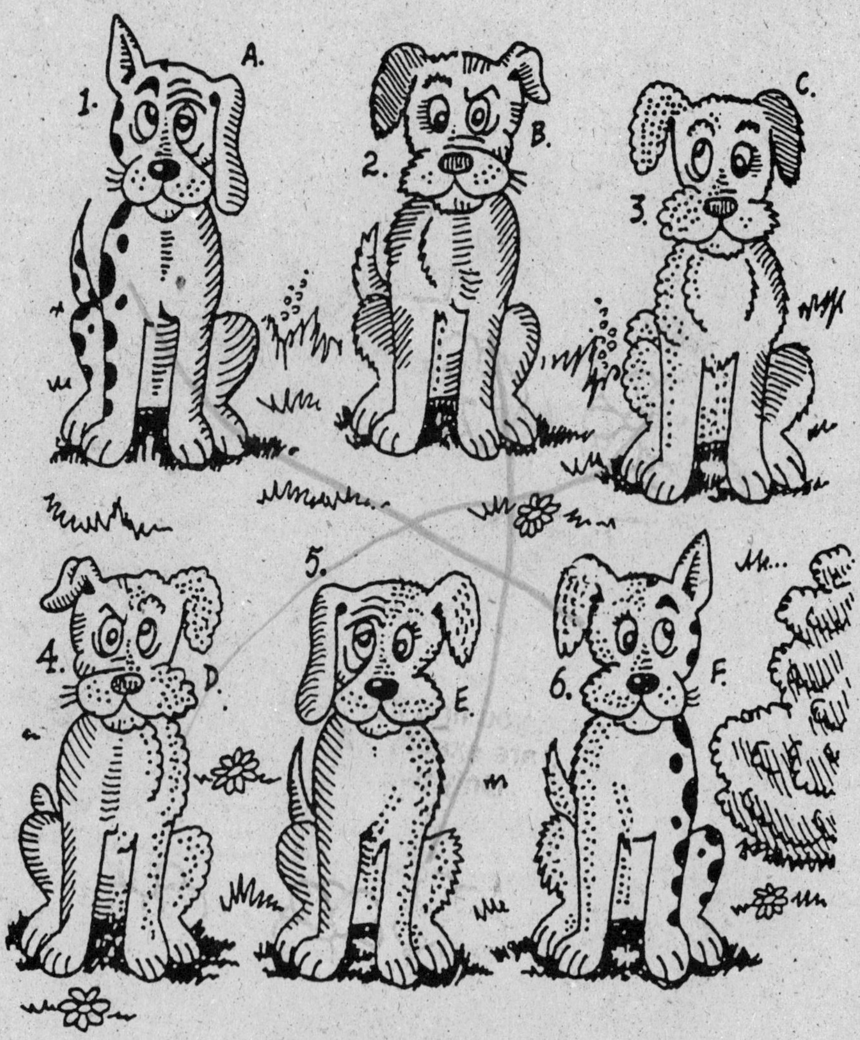

These six unfortunate mongrels have been split in half. Can you put the correct halves together?

123

Can you find the two that are exactly alike? Only two are.

124
Which sound effect goes with which cartoon?
A.
B.
SLURP!
1.
2. SMASH!
C.
3. BASH!
4. SPLASH!
D.
5. ZZZZZZ
E.
F.
6. BOING!

125
Can you tell how many things
in the bottom picture are
different from the top picture?
Look closely.
A

126

We have been having a birthday party. We're exhausted, and were just wondering if you would be good enough to help us count the amount of balloons that are left and to join the dots to find out what else is left of our party.

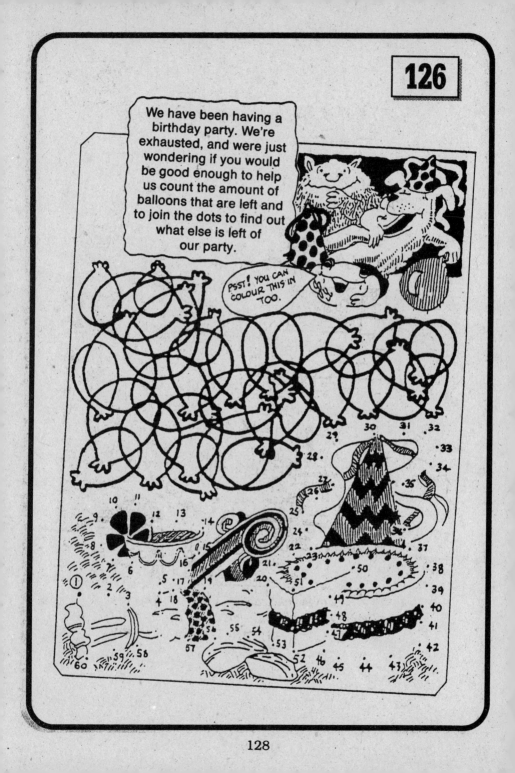

127

THE LITTLE NURSE

6A
5A
2D
1D
8A
3A
7D
4A

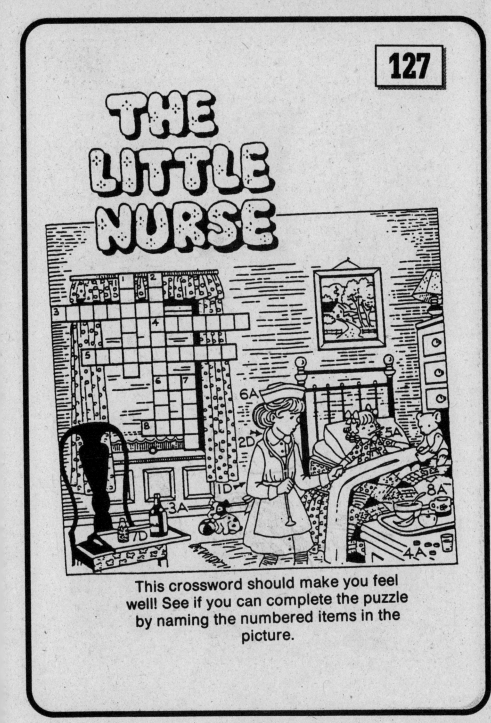

This crossword should make you feel well! See if you can complete the puzzle by naming the numbered items in the picture.

128

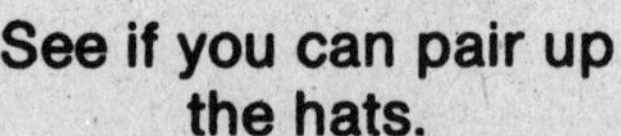

See if you can pair up the hats.

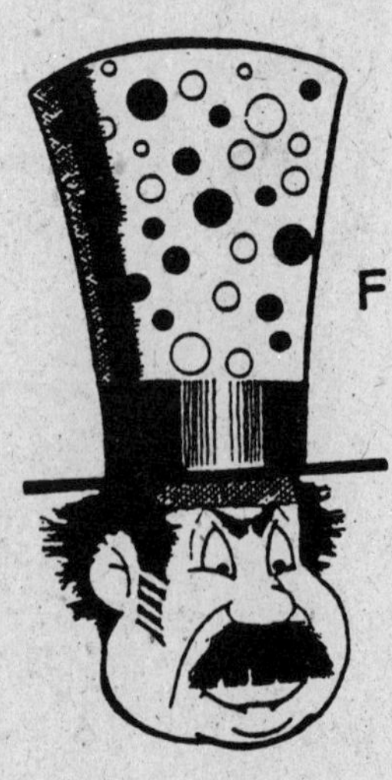

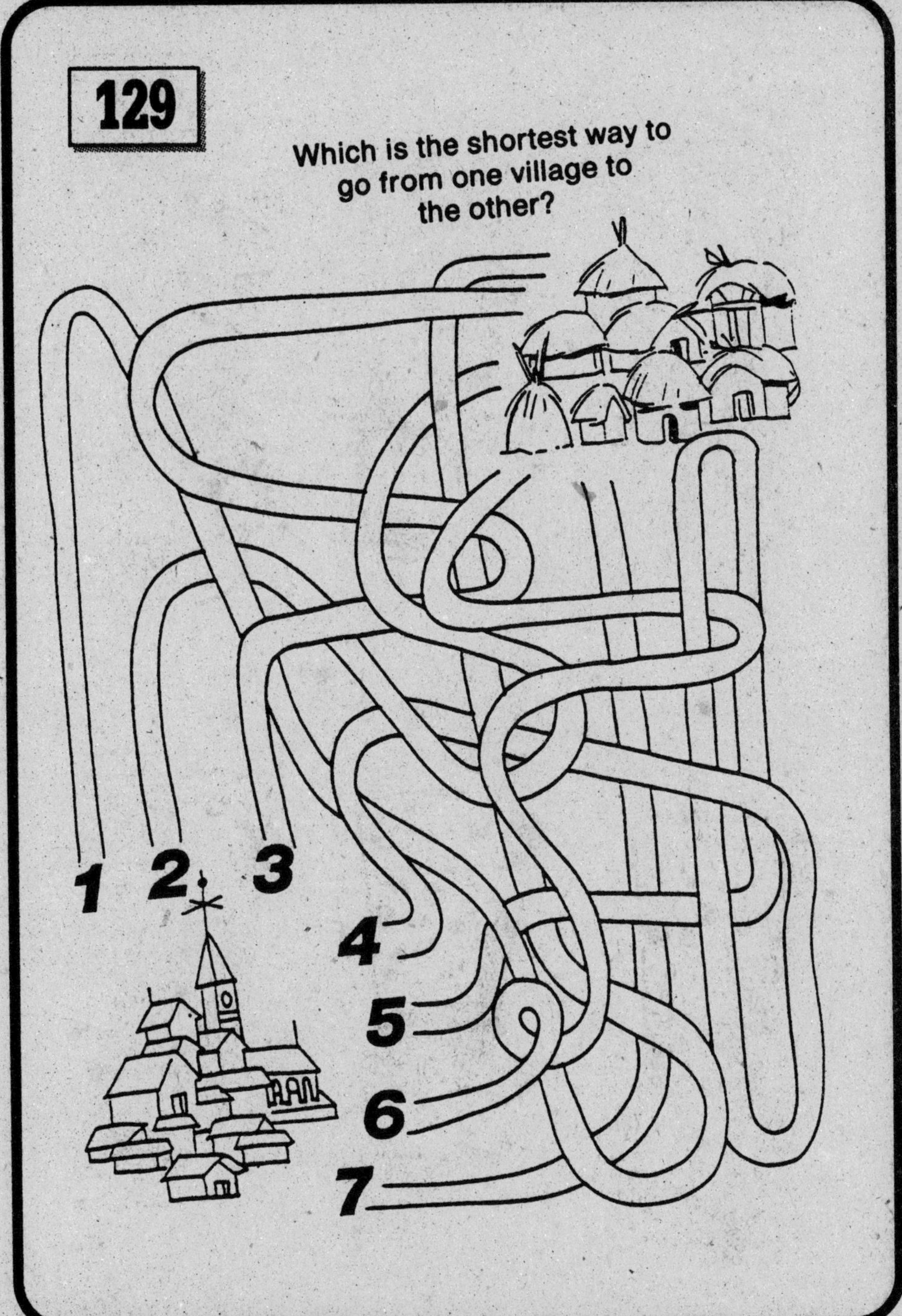
129
Which is the shortest way to
go from one village to
the other?
1
2
3
4
5
6
7

130

Find the continuous black line from the umbrella to the ice cream.

131

Take a pencil and redraw the shape in "A" in the blank square "1A". Do the same with A2, A3, etc. and you will form a picture!

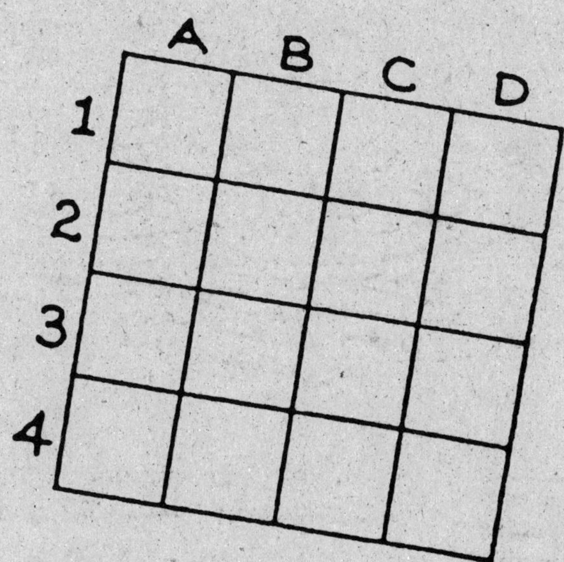

132

Can you see which piece fits into this drawing of a Mexican? There are four possibilities - A, B, C and D.

133

Can you see which piece fits into this picture? There are four possibilities – A, B, C and D.

134

Match the jumbled pictures on the right with the picture on the left to discover the man's name.

135

Join the dots from
No. 1 – 36 to find a hidden
picture.

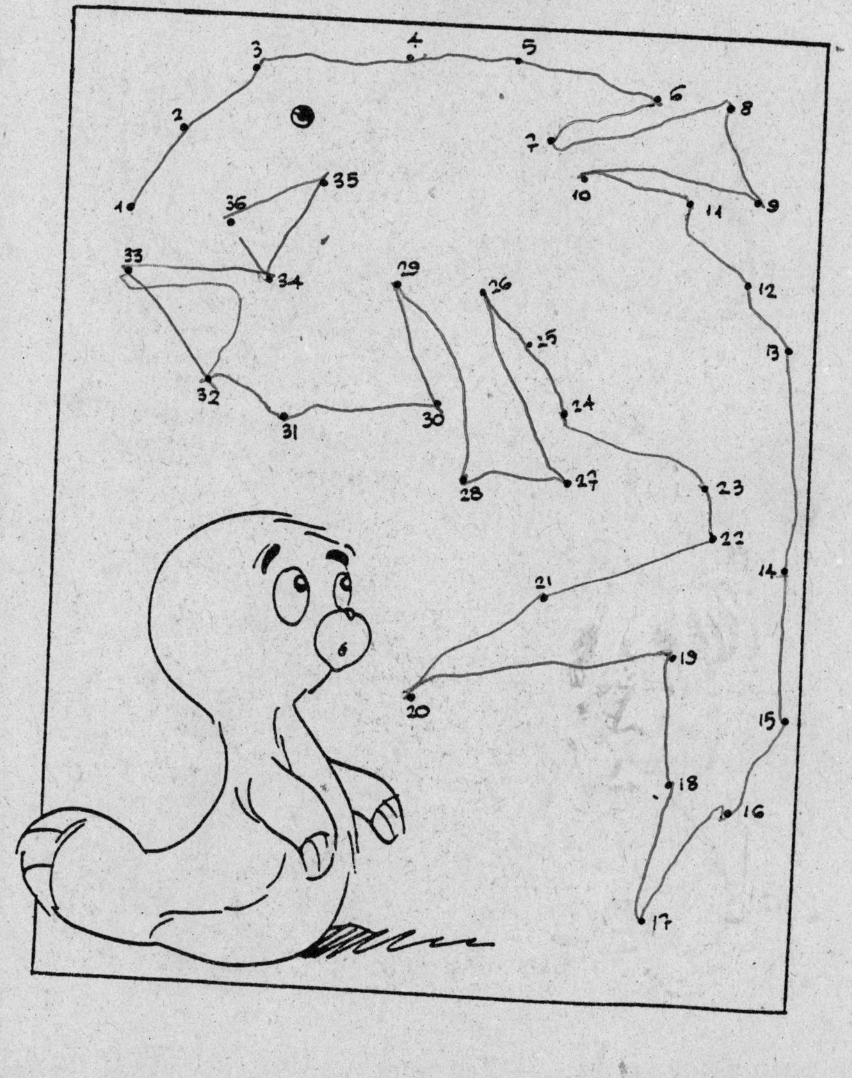

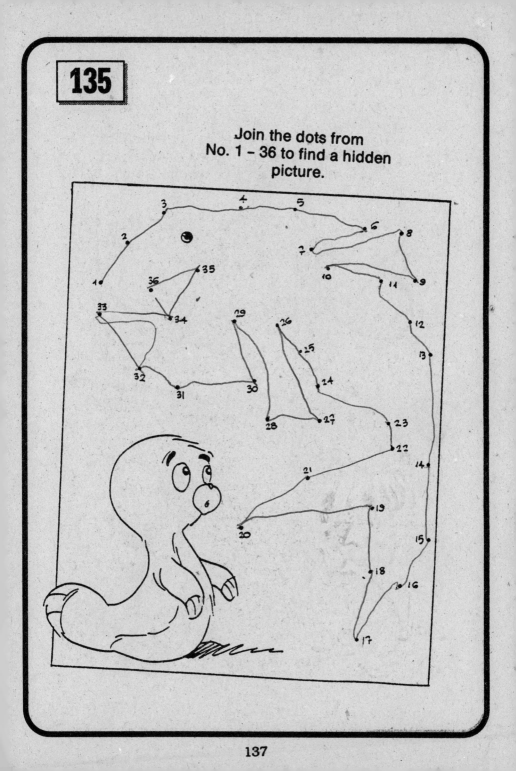

136

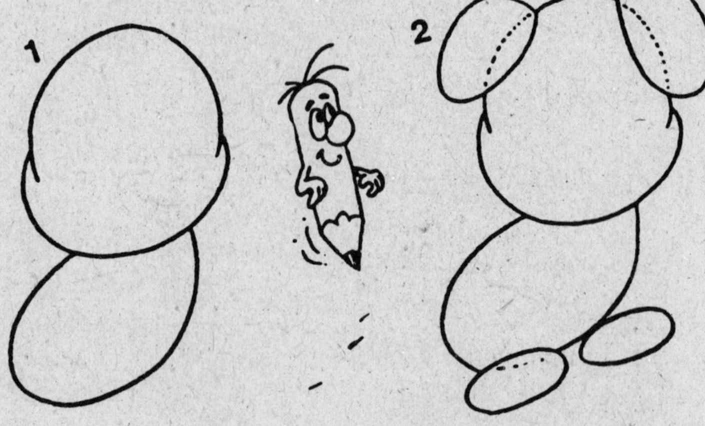
1
2

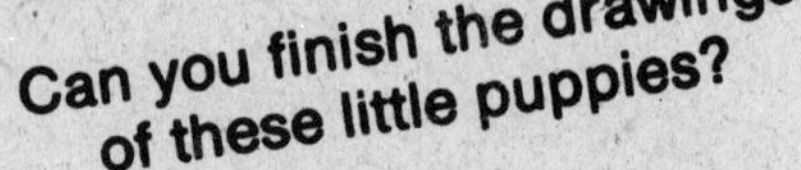
Can you finish the drawings
of these little puppies?

3

4

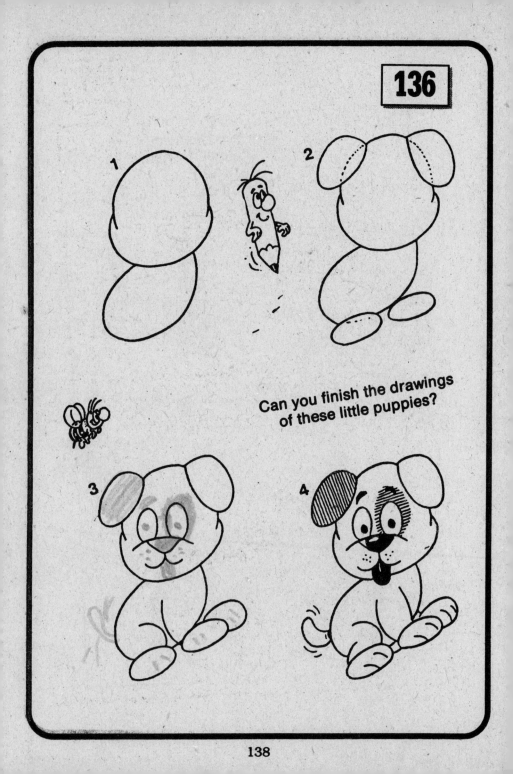

137

Spot 10 Differences Between The Two Pictures!!

138

Can you untangle the tentacles and tell which belongs to which?

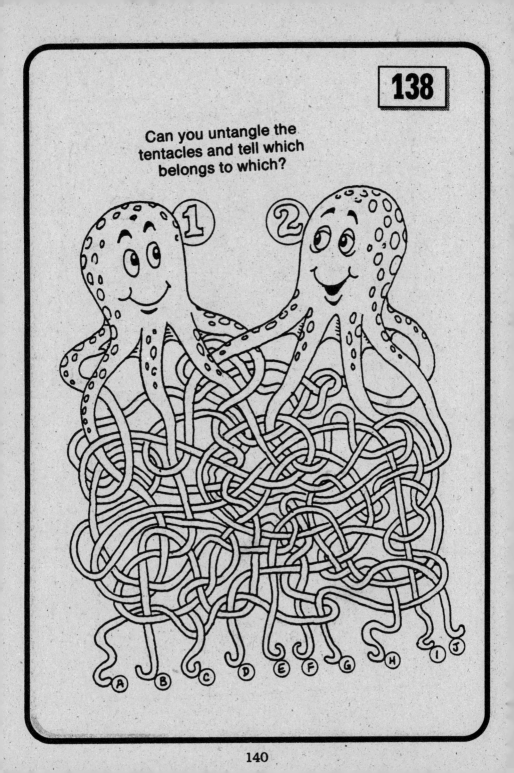

139

Memory test. (Cover the top picture and shade the bottom picture).

140

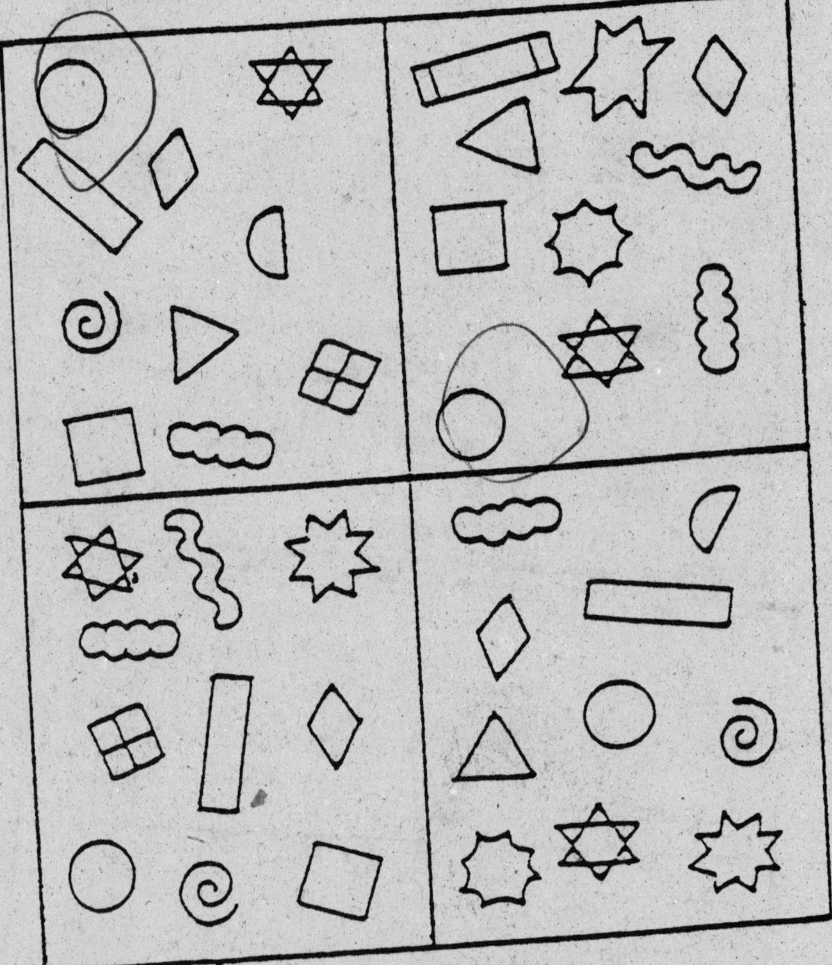

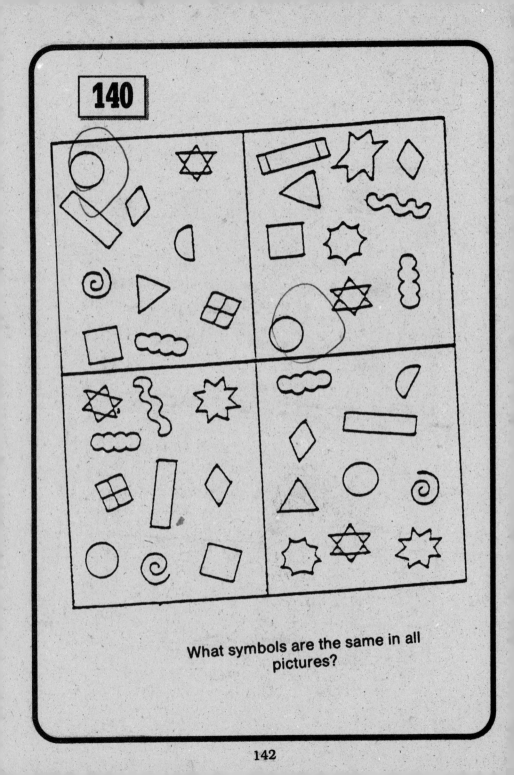

What symbols are the same in all pictures?

141
DRAW-IN THE OTHER HALF OF THE CAT TO FINISH THE PICTURE. GET DRAWING WITH THOSE PENCILS READERS!!

142

Using the pictures as clues, fill in the answers to complete the crossword.

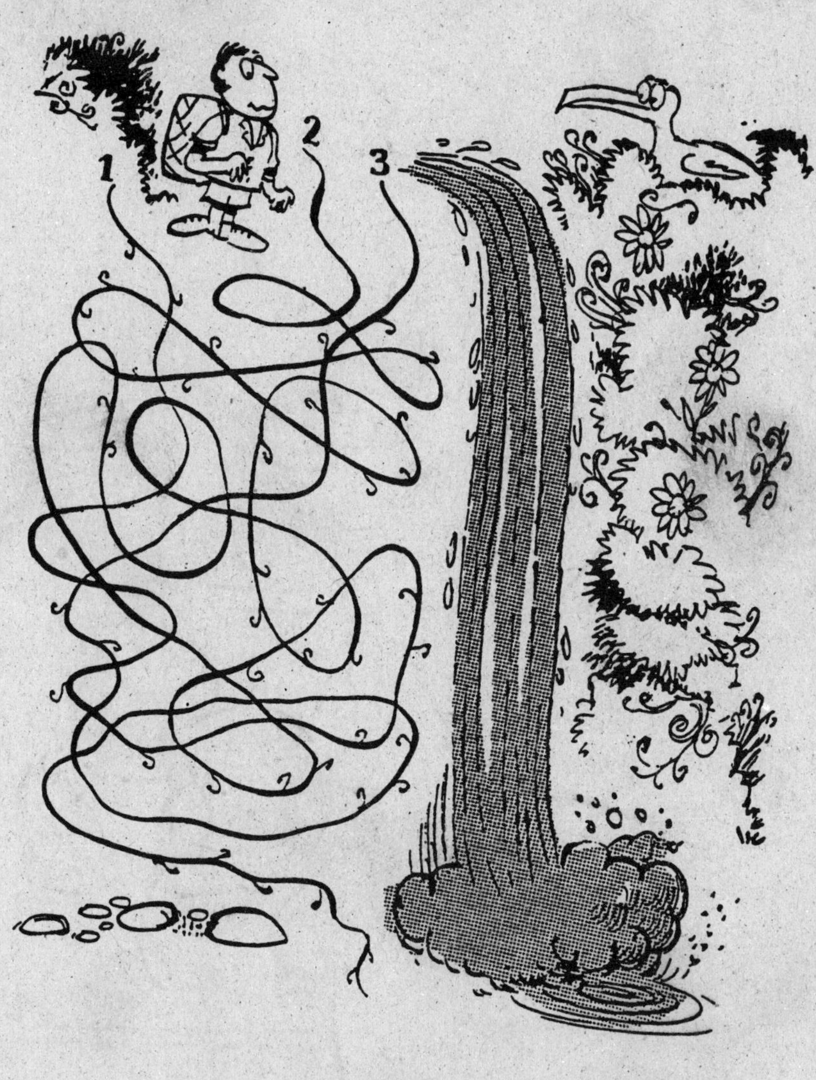

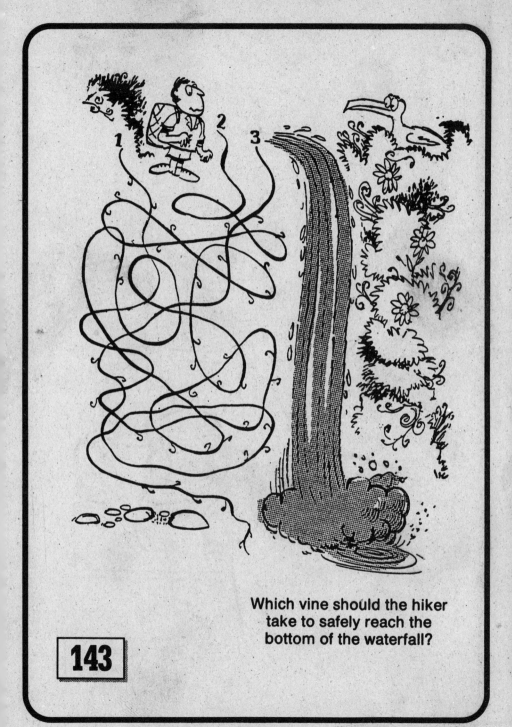

Which vine should the hiker take to safely reach the bottom of the waterfall?

143

CAN YOU SPOT FIVE OBJECTS THAT SHOULDN'T BE IN THE SUITCASE?

144

145

Complete the grid to spell five animals reading down each column.

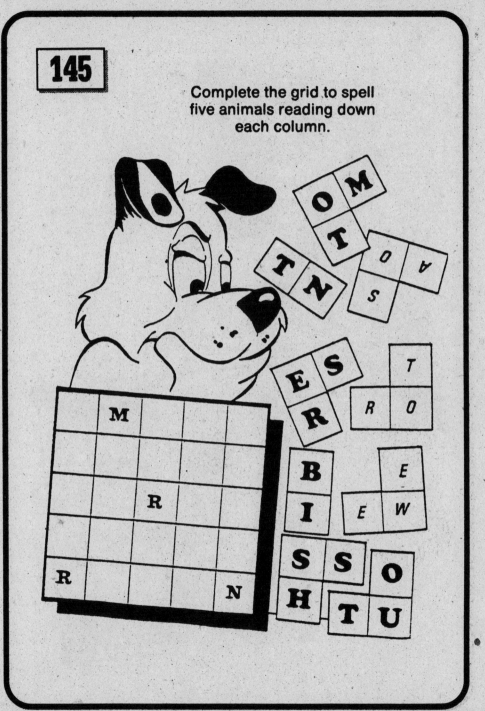

146

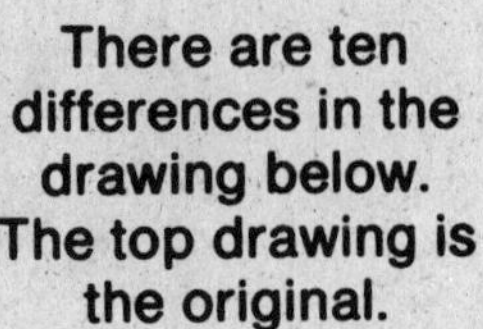

There are ten differences in the drawing below. The top drawing is the original.

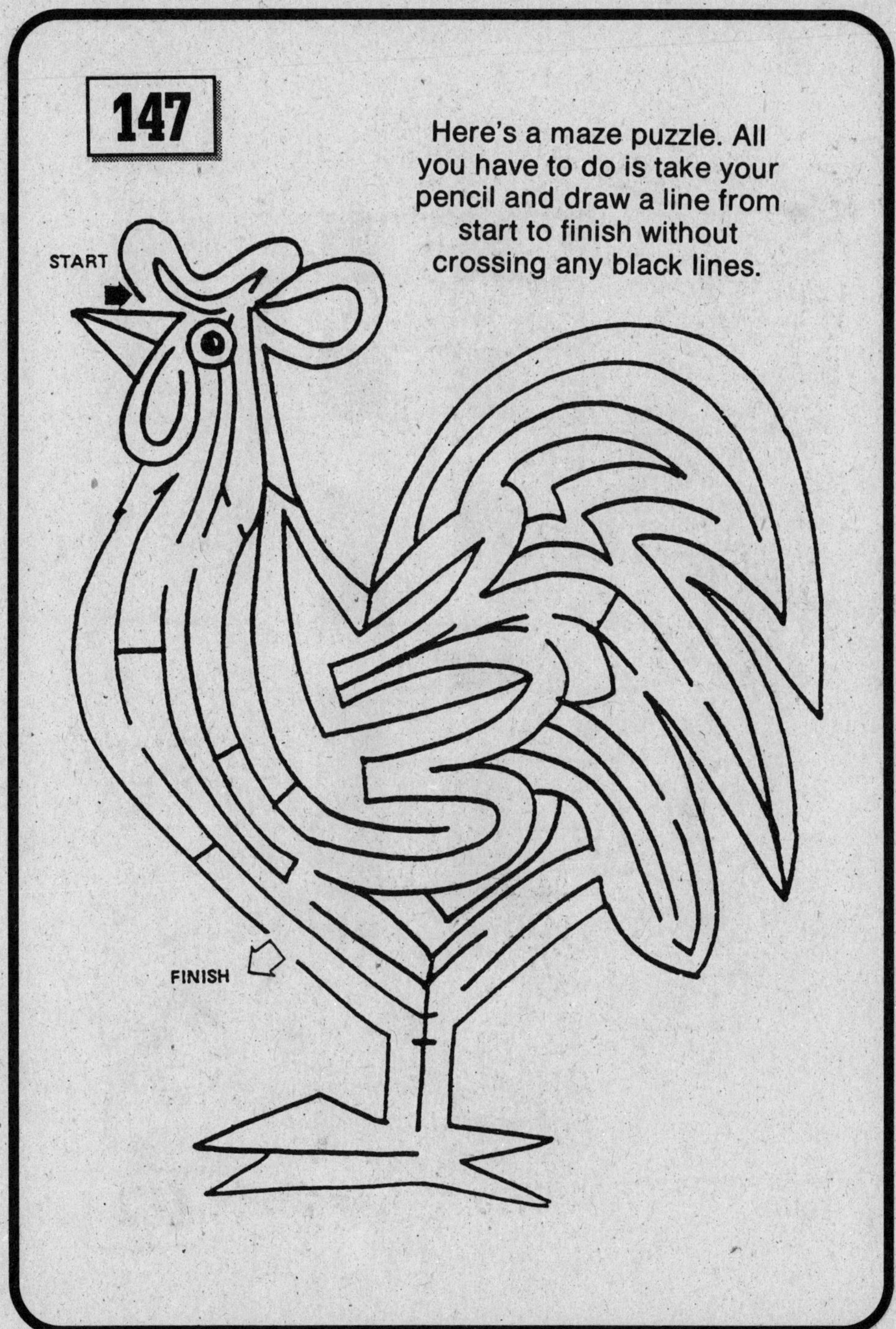
147
Here's a maze puzzle. All you have to do is take your pencil and draw a line from start to finish without crossing any black lines.
START
FINISH

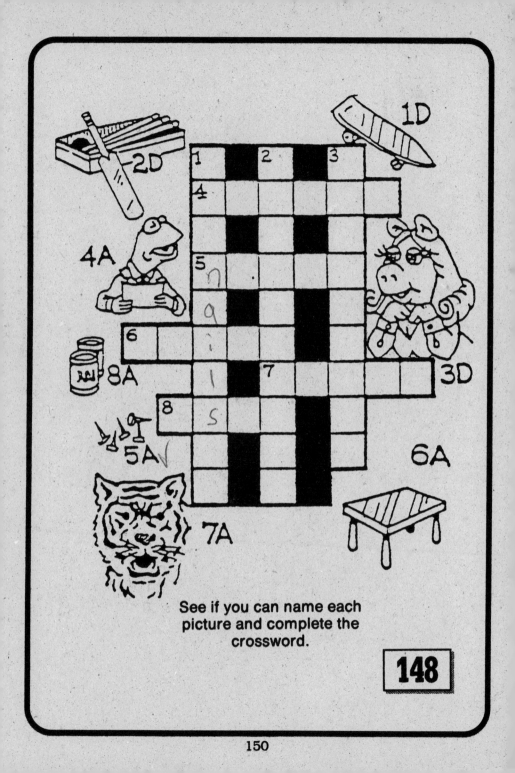

See if you can name each picture and complete the crossword.

148

149

Which two kittens are the same?

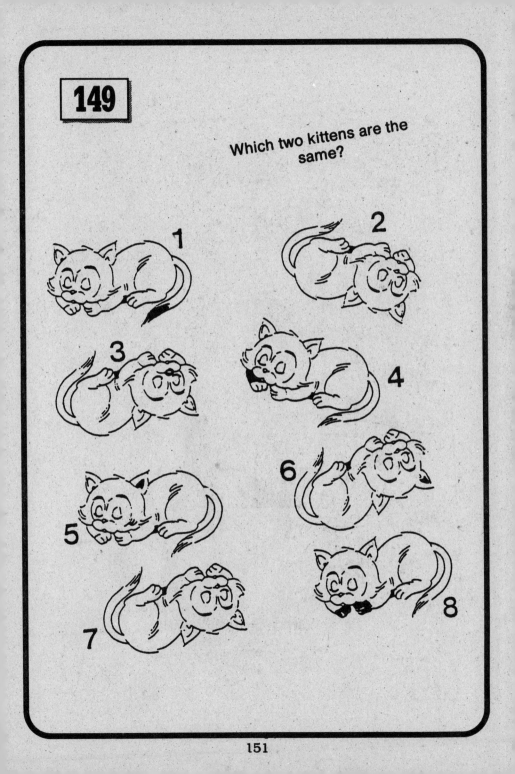

150

There are only two of these small boats that will fit perfectly into the bottle. Which ones?

151

These two archers really had a contest! Man, did those arrows fly! See if you can dodge the arrows below.

START

FINISH

152

Shade the spaces marked with dots and you will obtain a very attractive drawing.

CAMERA! ACTION!

To find out what the camera is filming, join up the dots starting at No. 1 and finishing at No. 87.

153

Can you get the two halves of the six eggs together?

154

There are ten differences in the two pictures of weather below. See if you can find them, (the left is the original) – then colour it in.

155

156
Crack the Code
18'14 20 9 22 26 7
26 7 8 12 15 5 18 13 20
11 6 1 1 15 22 8 18 13
7 19 22 17 6 13 18 12 9
11 6 1 1 15 22 25 12 12 16
26 A 25 B 24 C 23 D 22 E 21 F 20 G 19 H 18 I
17 J 16 K 15 L 14 M 13 N 12 O 11 P 10 Q 9 R
8 S 7 T 6 U 5 V 4 W 3 X 2 Y 1 Z

157

Try to find out on which island the pirate's treasure is hidden. You have to go through 8 circles, and the total number of the eight circles when added together, must be 30.

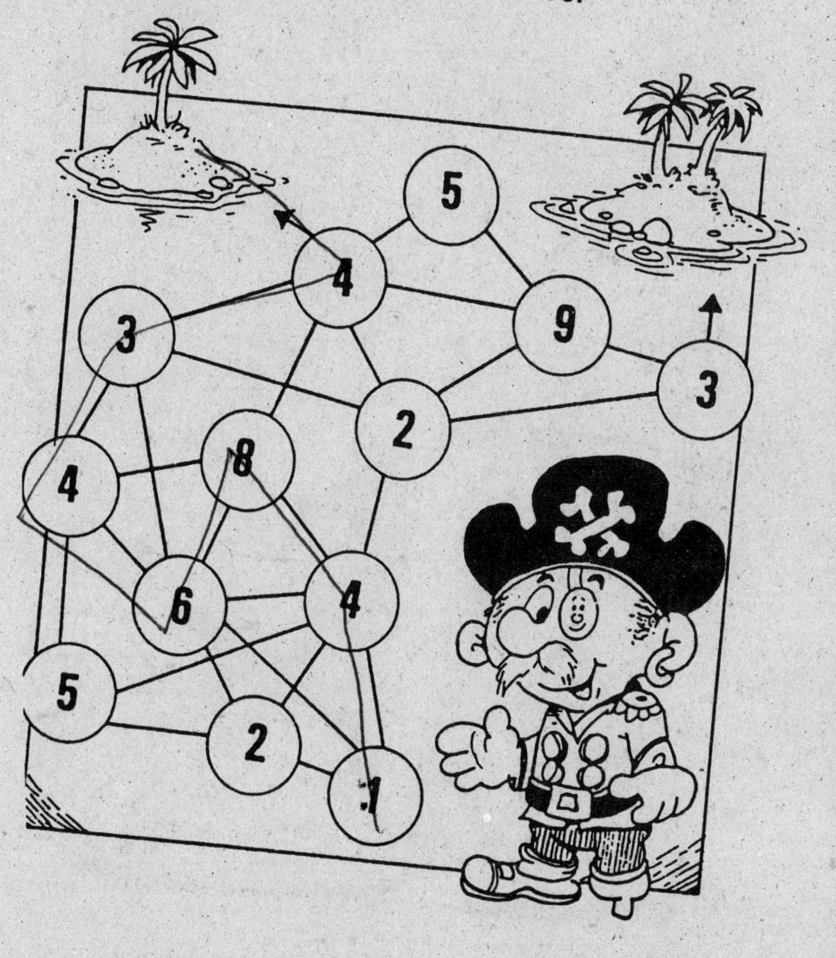

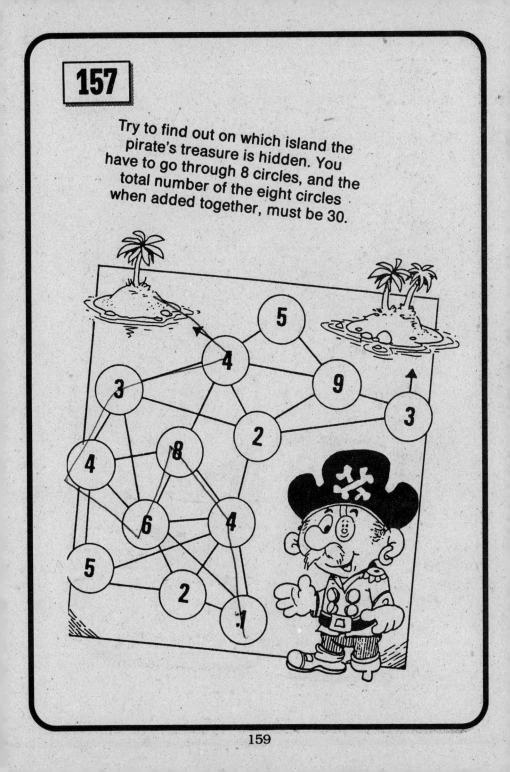

158

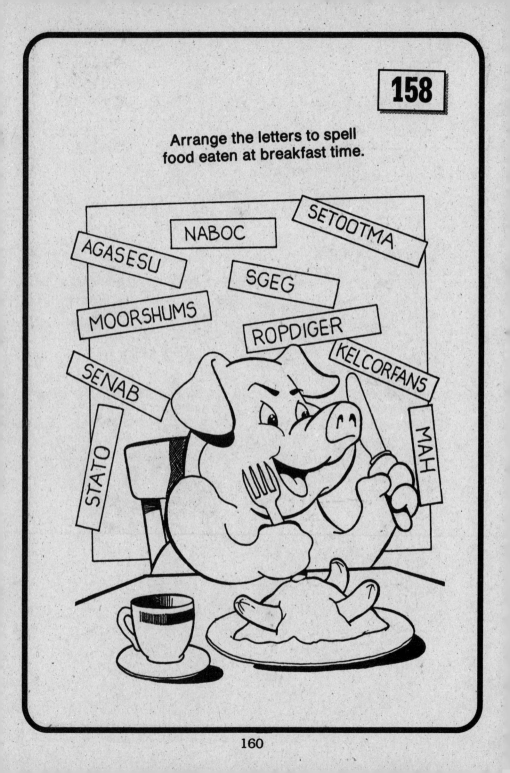

Arrange the letters to spell food eaten at breakfast time.

159

Below there are a number of people who normally perform in pairs. Here they are shown individually – but who pairs with whom?

A Hamlet | **a Juliet**
B Romeo | **b Bess**
C Paris | **c Ophelia**
D Porgy | **d Helena**

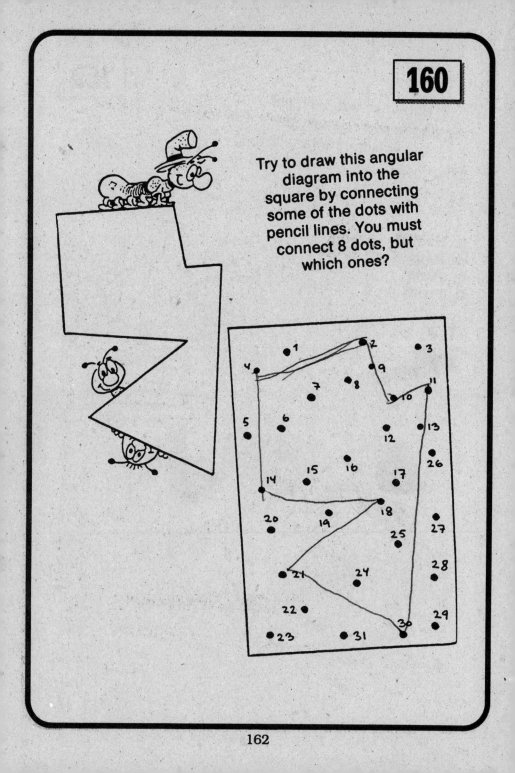

160

Try to draw this angular diagram into the square by connecting some of the dots with pencil lines. You must connect 8 dots, but which ones?

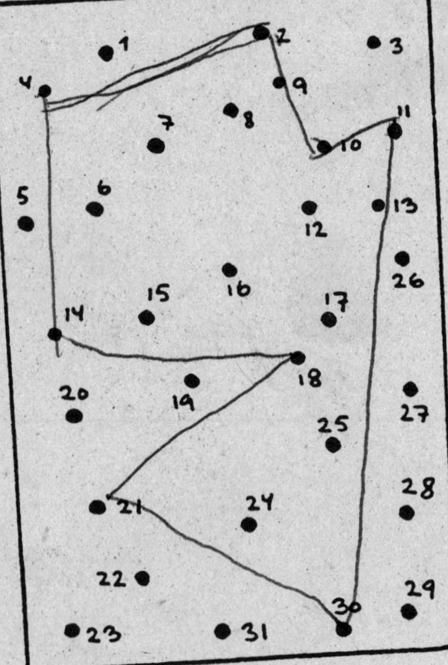

161

Shade in the dotted shapes.

COLOU
IN!
BOING!
SHOVE!
162

163

Which duck is the odd one out?

164

How many things can you find in this picture that start with the magic letter A? Circle all the things you find.

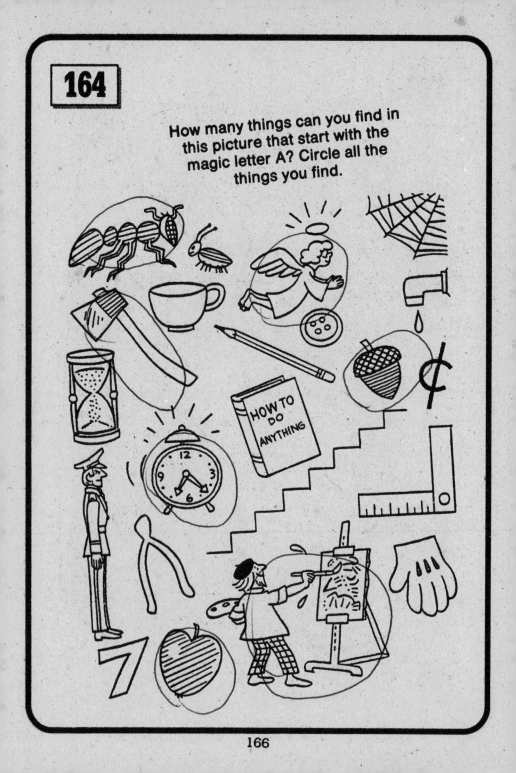

165

Can you tell how many things in the bottom picture are different from the top picture? Look closely!

166
Find the pattern which appears most, then re-arrange their letters to spell a name.
F
L
Y
H
L
K
E
G
A
M
T
N
O
V
R
LAMPITT

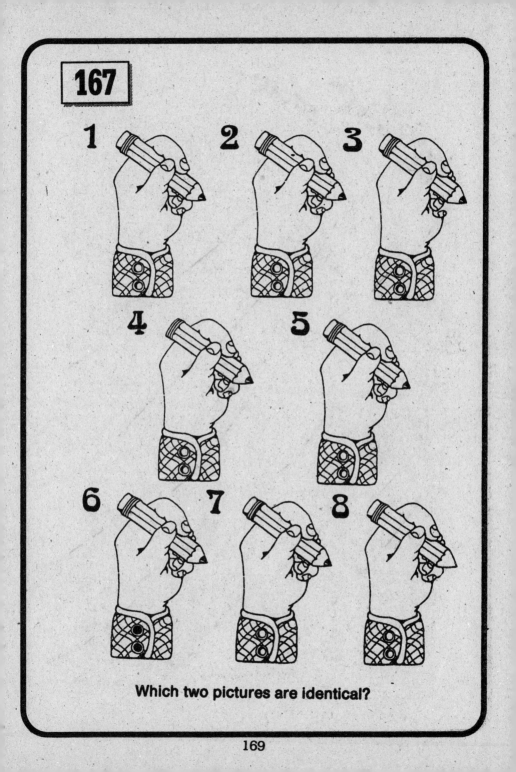

167

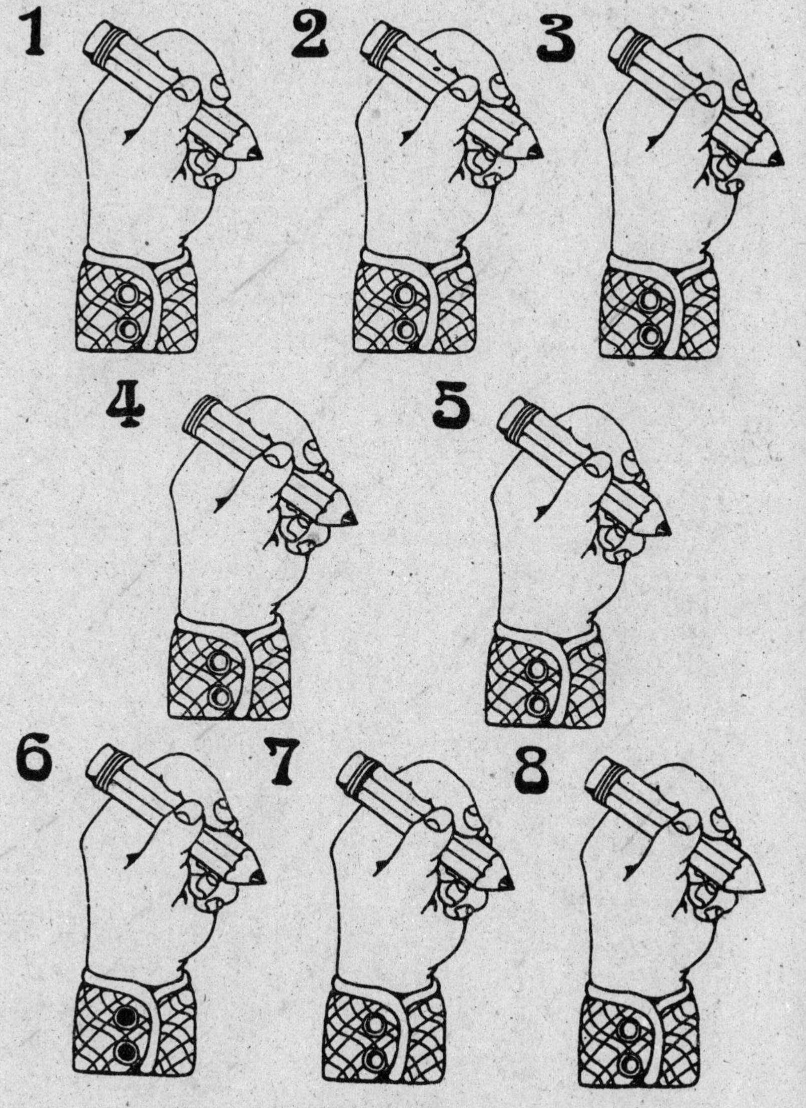

Which two pictures are identical?

168

Moving from square 1 - 2 - 3 - 4 etc. use the initial letters to make four boys' names.

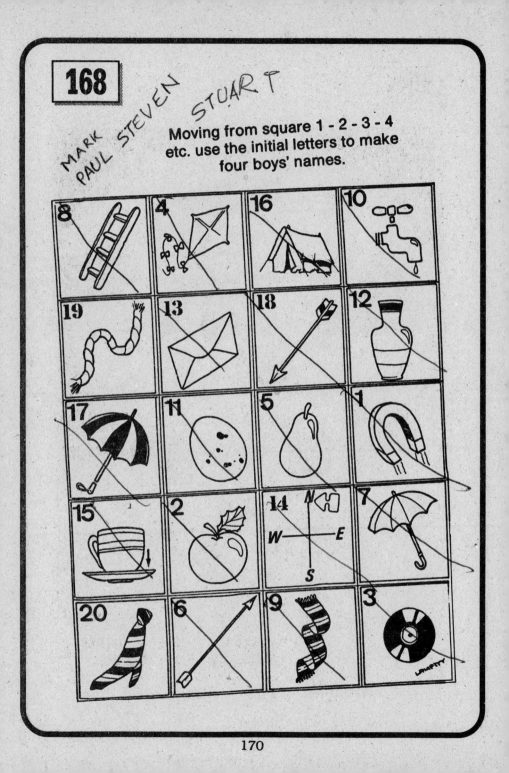

169

Join the dots from 1 to 39 to discover a hidden picture.

170

Help the squirrel through this ladder maze.

171

Which two pictures are identical?

172

Our artist has mixed up these four drawings. Can you place the right legs on the correct person?

173

How many autumn leaves are there to rake up?

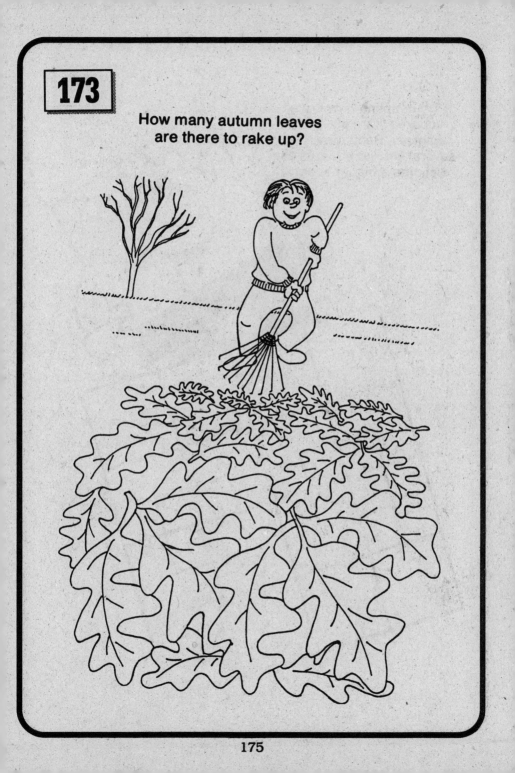

174
Try counting how many squares there are in this diagram. Remember that several smaller squares can become a bigger square.
GIL

There are seven differences in the second picture. Can you spot them?

175

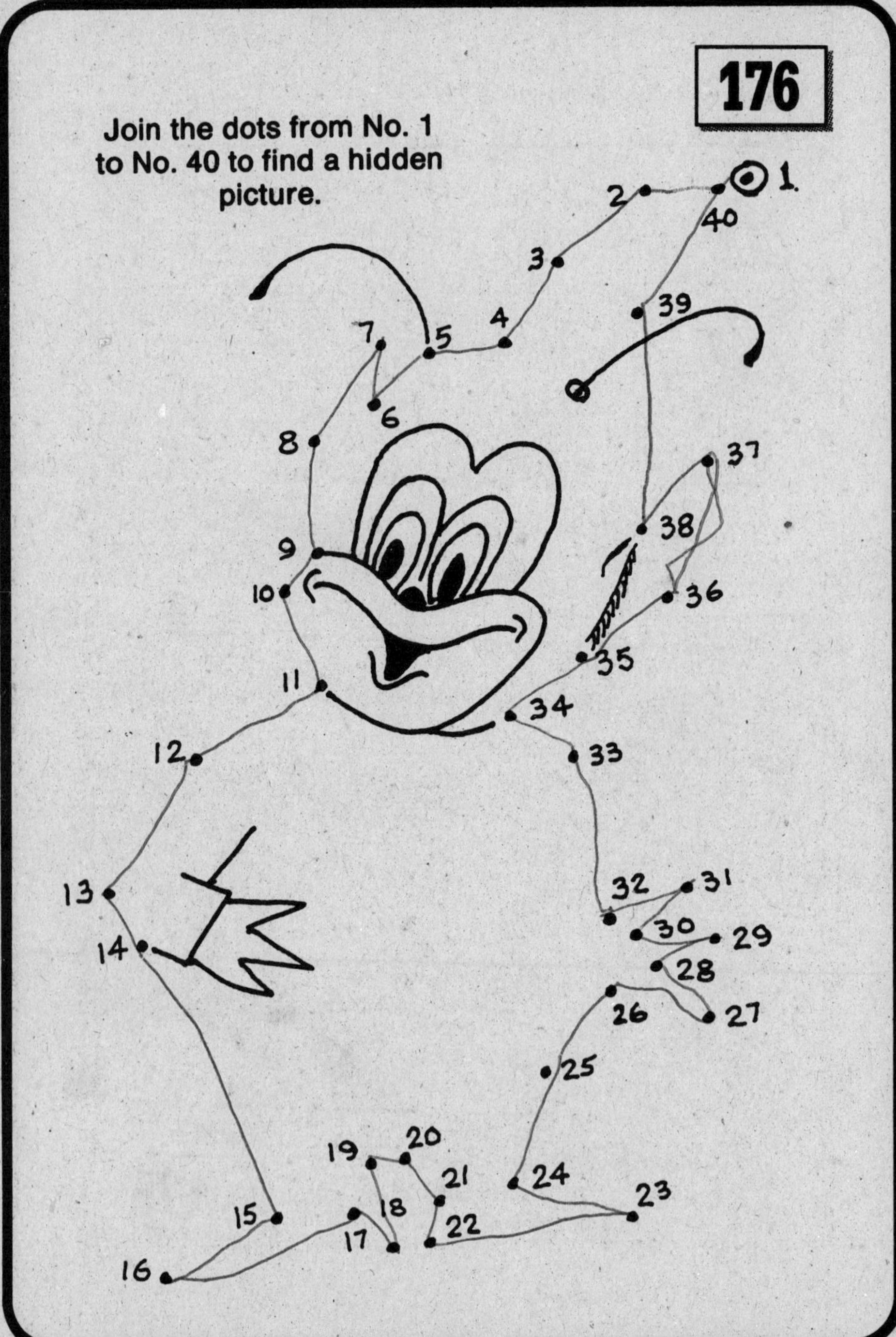
176
Join the dots from No. 1 to No. 40 to find a hidden picture.
1
2
3
4
5
6
7
8
9
10
11
12
13
14
15
16
17
18
19
20
21
22
23
24
25
26
27
28
29
30
31
32
33
34
35
36
37
38
39
40

177

Pair the items which rhyme.

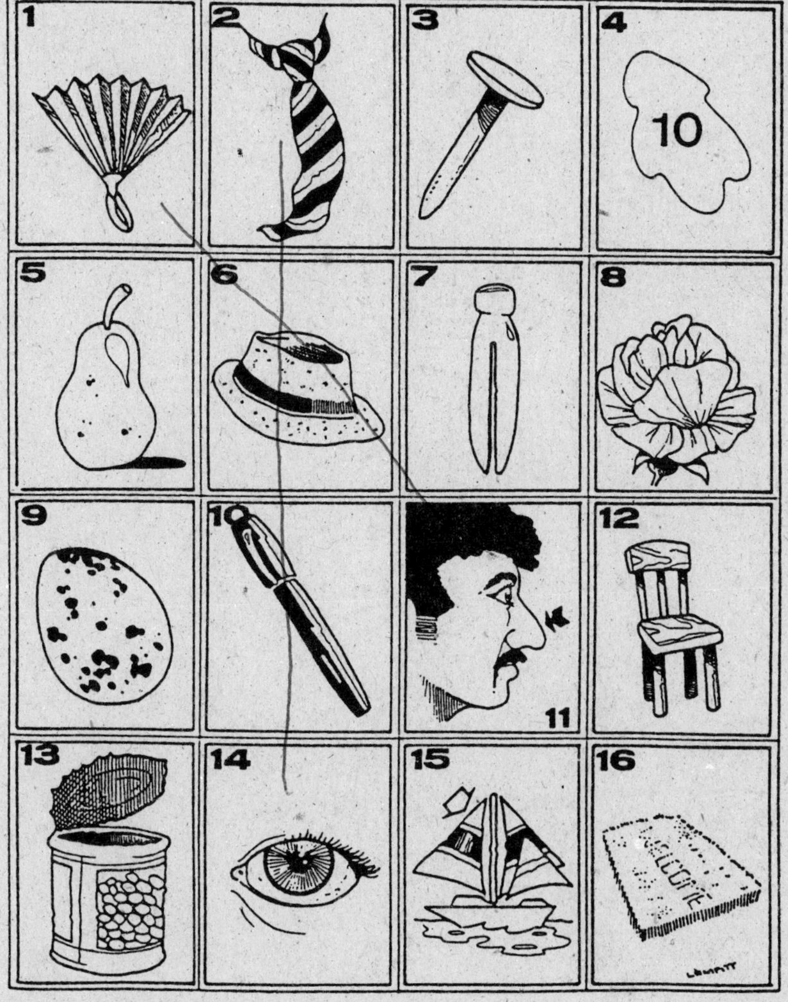

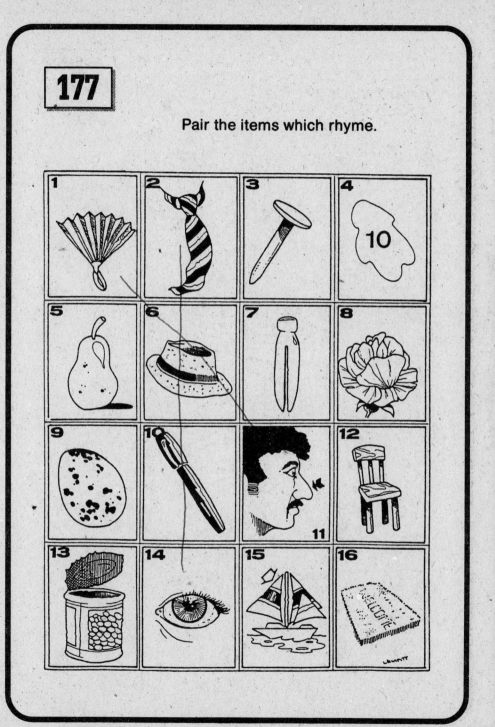

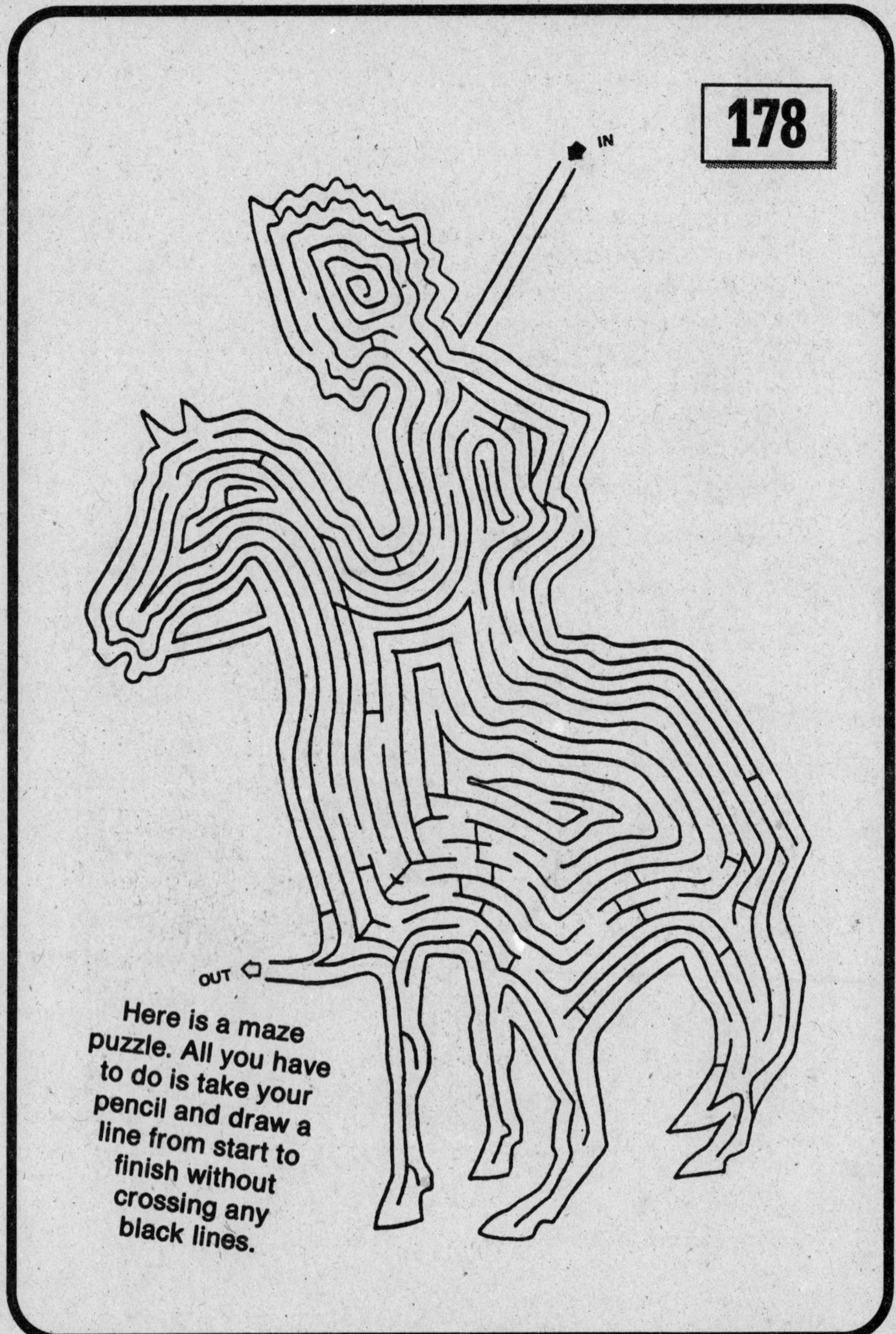
178
IN
OUT
Here is a maze puzzle. All you have to do is take your pencil and draw a line from start to finish without crossing any black lines.

179

If you slowly lower your nose right down to the rowing boat while looking at the little star, you will be very surprised to see the steamship become a whole ship again. Try making some similar drawings yourself. For instance, a collapsed bridge which becomes whole again, or an aeroplane flying into a black cloud. There are many possibilities.

180

How many things begin with "C"?

181

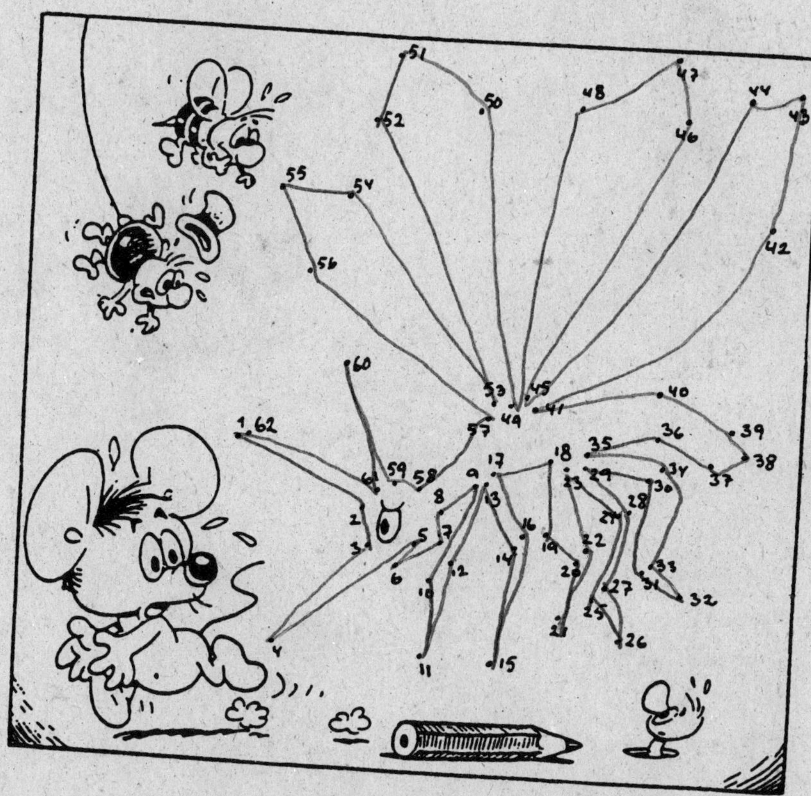

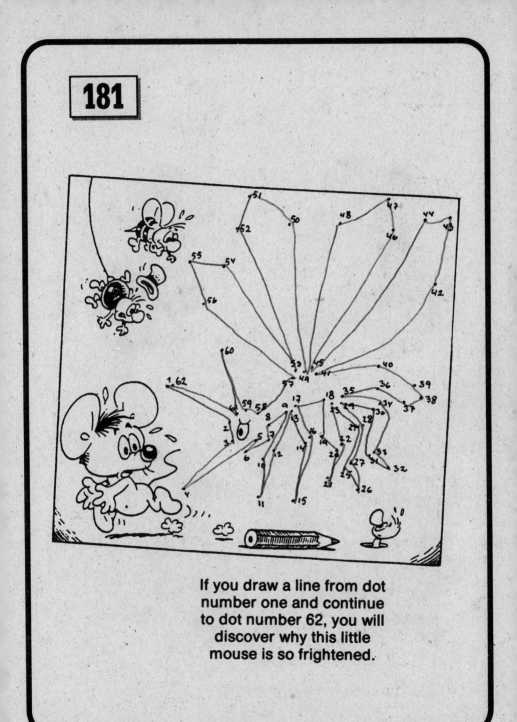

If you draw a line from dot number one and continue to dot number 62, you will discover why this little mouse is so frightened.

182

Which shadow belongs to the duck?

183

Most people like to see what the painting is supposed to be, so in this case the artist has made it easy for us. But he hasn't been too particular about the small details. What has he done wrong? Look carefully and you'll find 7 mistakes.

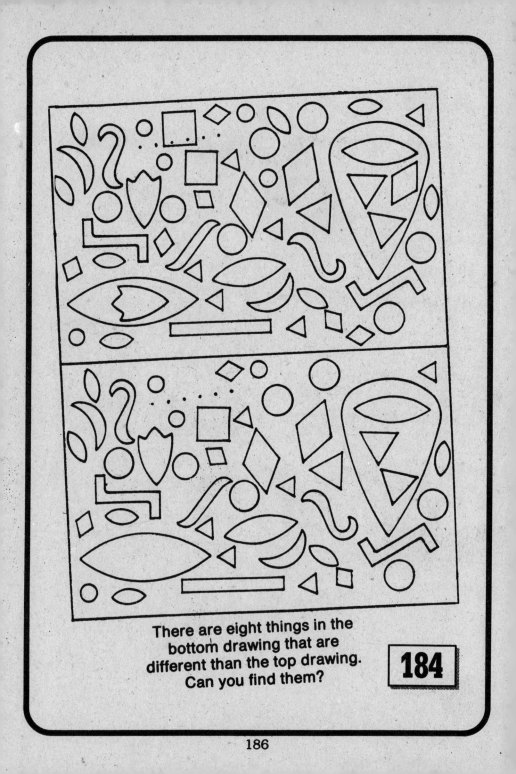

There are eight things in the bottom drawing that are different than the top drawing. Can you find them?

184

Our artist has mixed up these four drawings. Can you place the right legs on the correct person?

185

186

Assemble the grid to find eight animals and birds.

187

At first glance it would seem that all these heads are alike, but only one of the heads fits the black silhouette. Perhaps it's a little difficult to find the right one, but then it wouldn't be so much fun if it was easy, would it?

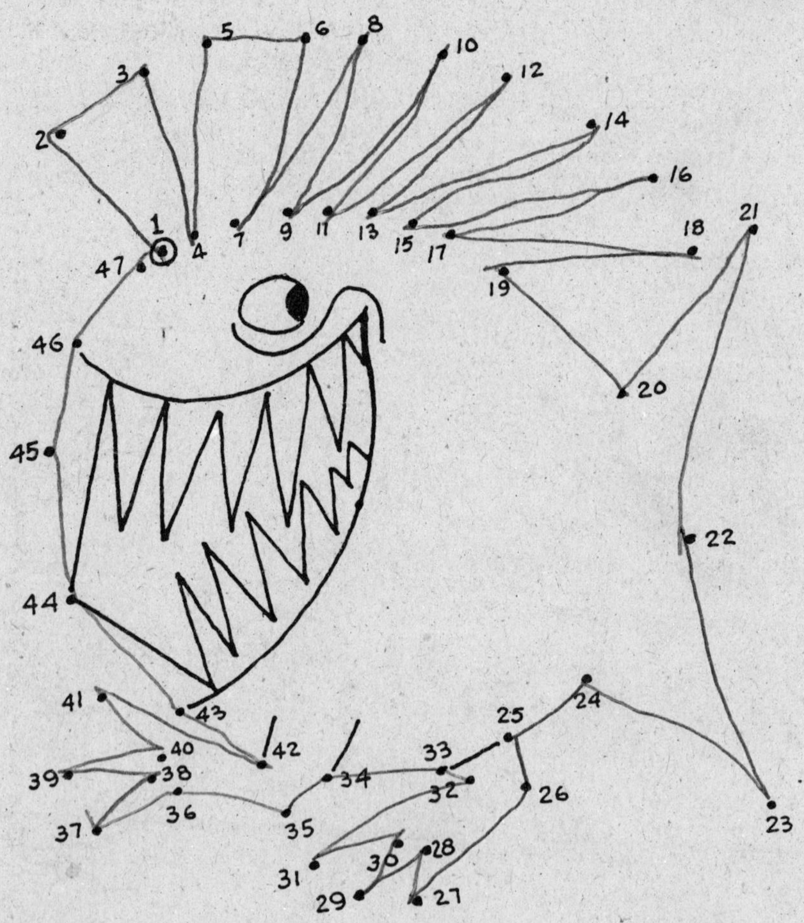

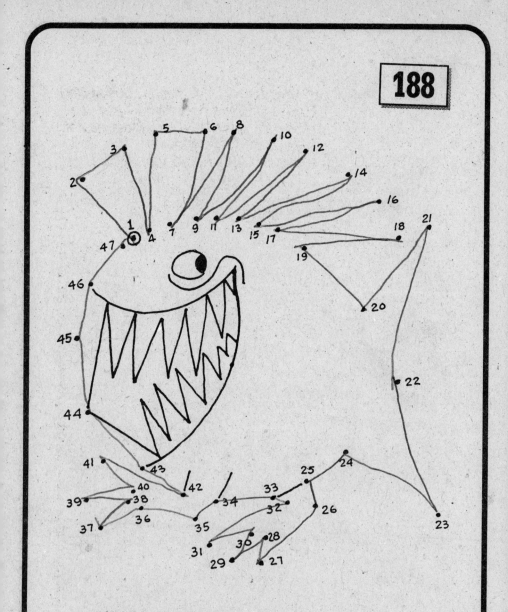

Join the dots from No. 1 to No. 47 to find a hidden picture.

189

Starting at No. 1, take your pencil and connect all the dots. When you are finished, you will have made a secret picture.

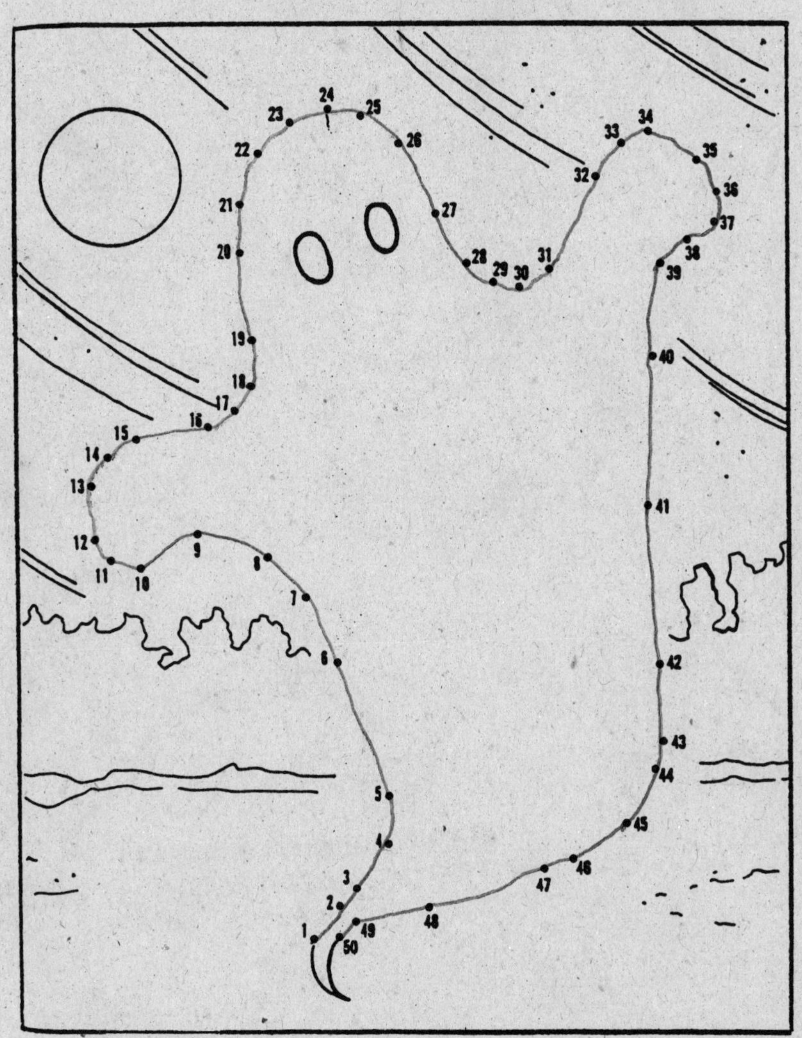

190

Can you remove five circles from the picture and still leave four circles in each row?

SOLUTIONS

PUZZLE 1

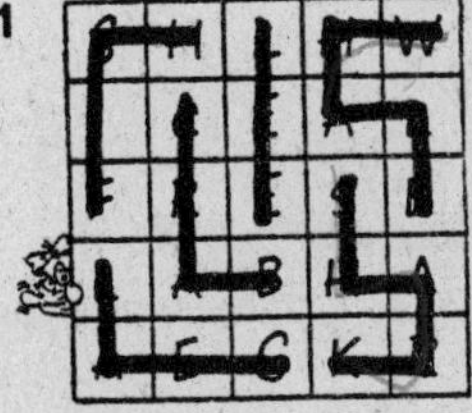

PUZZLE 2

1. Cloud, 2. Sun, 3. Bird, 4. Rain, 5. House, 6. Cow, 7. Tree, 8. River.

PUZZLE 4

PUZZLE 5

PUZZLE 6

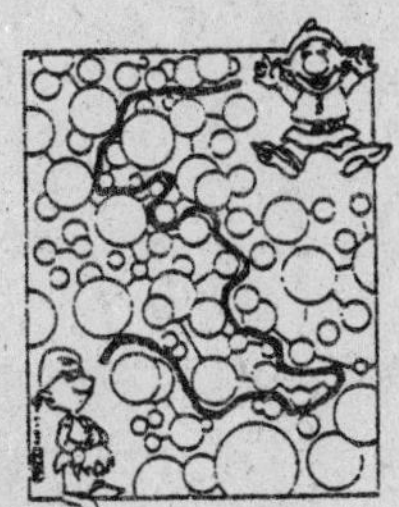

PUZZLE 7

No. 6.

PUZZLE 8

Tunnel D.

PUZZLE 10

PUZZLE 11

Doves-Gloves, Roots-Boots, Toggles-Goggles, Chicks-Sticks, Cat-Hat, Knees-Skis.

PUZZLE 12

SOLUTIONS

PUZZLE 13

A–J, B–E, C–I, F–H, D–G.

PUZZLE 14

4–Daffodils, 5–Daisies, 6–Tulips.

PUZZLE 15

PUZZLE 16

Shape No. 2.

PUZZLE 17

Remove numbers 8, 11 and 14.

PUZZLE 19

PUZZLE 20

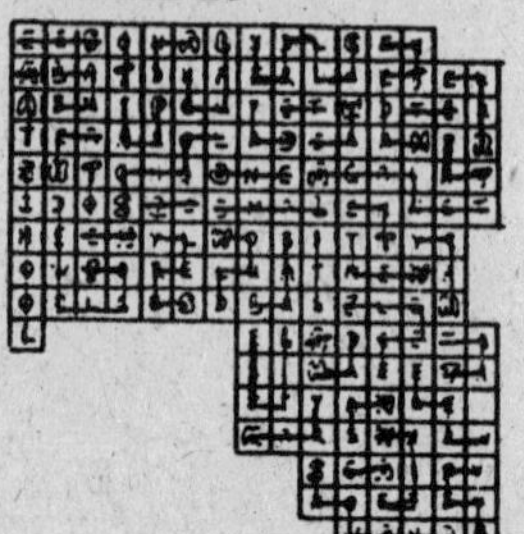

PUZZLE 21

Rope D.

PUZZLE 22

3 + 7 = 10 feet.

PUZZLE 23

Beach, Sand, Sandcastle, Starfish, Sea.

PUZZLE 24

Football, Cricket, Tennis, Hockey, Badminton, Baseball, Rugby, Croquet, Golf, Archery, Darts, Snooker, Chess, Shooting.

PUZZLE 25

S	S	E	R	T	C	A	E	P	S	L
P	L	C	M	O	S	D	P	A	M	S
C	S	D	P	L	T	A	M	R	D	E
L	M	I	C	S	P	C	S	E	G	M
C	L	R	A	R	E	M	A	C	N	U
P	S	E	C	M	L	C	P	U	I	T
D	M	C	I	P	C	S	L	D	T	S
R	A	T	S	L	P	S	C	O	H	O
D	P	O	U	C	M	L	S	R	G	C
L	S	R	M	A	D	M	C	P	I	P
C	M	D	A	P	L	S	A	D	L	S

PUZZLE 26

23 feathers.

PUZZLE 27

C2-F4, A7-B4, A1-D7, D1-E5, G5-G7, B6-F9.

PUZZLE 28

SOLUTIONS

PUZZLE 29

5B-8F, 7F-9B, 3A-4D, 1C-3G, 5G-9D, 1G-2A.

PUZZLE 30

Frank Bruno - Boxing, Steve Davis - Snooker, Ian Botham - Cricket, John Barnes - Football, Nigel Mansell - Motor Racing, Steffi Graf -Tennis, Will Carling - Rugby.

PUZZLE 31

31 Pencils.

PUZZLE 32

1. Rug, 2. Egg, 3. Lamp, 4. Bee, 5. Octopus, 6. Umbrella, 7. Rake, 8. Nine, 9. Emu - MELBOURNE.

PUZZLE 33

2F-4E, 1D-8C, 4A-5F, 5D-9F, 2D-8A, 5B-8D.

PUZZLE 34

PUZZLE 35

PUZZLE 37

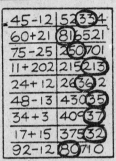

45-12	52334
60+21	816521
75-25	250701
11+202	215213
24+12	26362
48-13	43035
34+3	40937
17+15	37532
92-12	80710

PUZZLE 38

1-E and D, 2-F and B, 3-A and C.

PUZZLE 40

D, A, C and B.

PUZZLE 41

Ship A.

PUZZLE 42

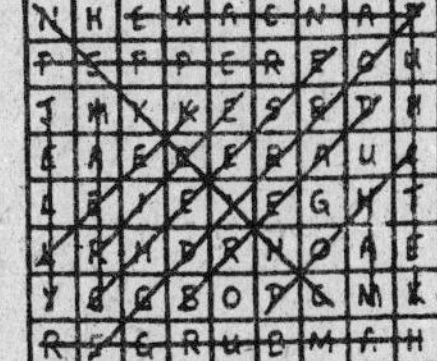

Chef's name - Hugo.

PUZZLE 43

CAN YOU HELP ME TO REACH MY HOME ON THE LEAF IN THE FAR CORNER OF THE GARDEN?
A
B
C
D

SOLUTIONS

PUZZLE 44

PUZZLE 45

PUZZLE 46

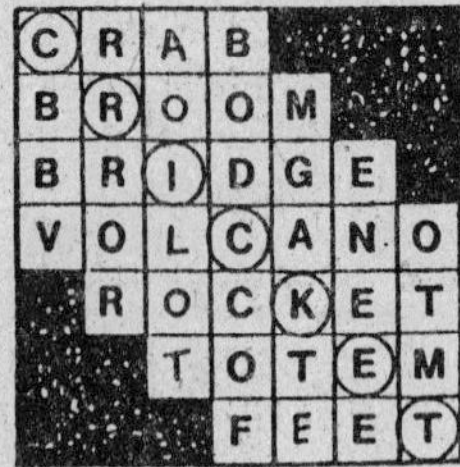

PUZZLE 47

40 ovals.

PUZZLE 48

Trilby.

PUZZLE 49

Harry.

PUZZLE 50

27 bubbles.

PUZZLE 51

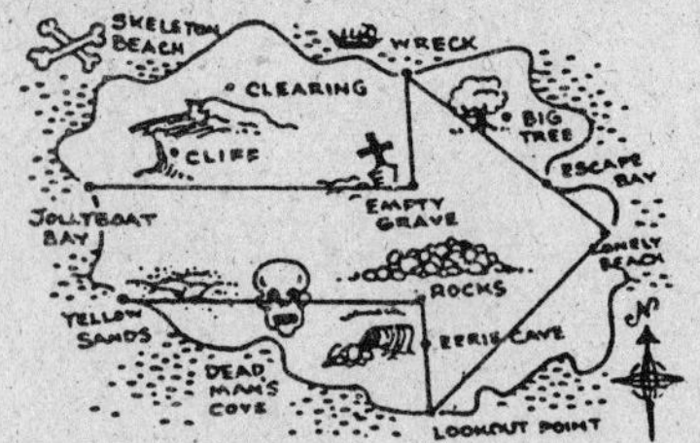

Lonely Beach.
The treasure is: Jewellery.

PUZZLE 52

PUZZLE 53

Bug-Mug, Lips-Chips, Fly-Eye, Trumpet-Crumpet, Cube-Tube, Claw-Saw.

PUZZLE 54

SOLUTIONS

PUZZLE 55

PUZZLE 56

5 and 7.

PUZZLE 57

PUZZLE 58

H, I, A, L, G, D, K, F, C, J, E, B.

PUZZLE 59

PUZZLE 60

3–7, 1–5, 6–4, 2–8.

PUZZLE 61

PUZZLE 62

1 and 5.

PUZZLE 63

Starting from the house, walk to the crossroads and turn left, follow the road towards the three trees. The treasure is buried under the large stone opposite.

PUZZLE 64

SOLUTIONS

PUZZLE 65

6 patterns.

PUZZLE 66

The moon. (The correct pair is STAR/SUN, as the sun is a star).

PUZZLE 67

PUZZLE 68

Line C.

PUZZLE 69

Shadow A.

PUZZLE 70

Too many cooks spoil the broth.

PUZZLE 71

PUZZLE 72

PUZZLE 73

PUZZLE 74

Hello

PUZZLE 75

The clown is wearing the dwarf's chain and the girl's bow.

PUZZLE 76

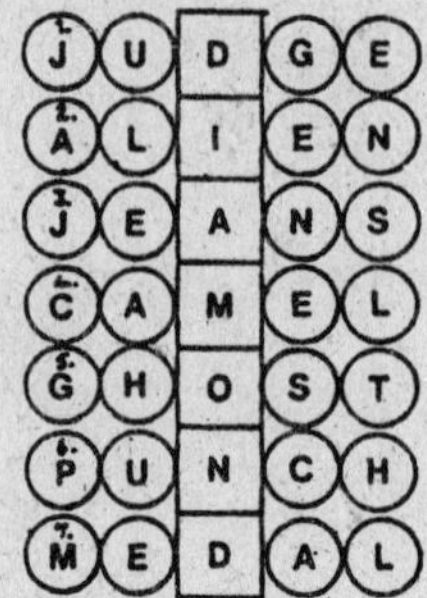

PUZZLE 77

No. 5

SOLUTIONS

PUZZLE 79
Route No. 2.

PUZZLE 80
Route C.

PUZZLE 81
12 shoes.

PUZZLE 83
Across: 2. Like, 4. New, 5. Book, 8. And, 9. Sad.
Down: 1. Were, 2. Look, 3. Round, 6. Taste, 7. Mad.

PUZZLE 84
What do you call a boomerang that won't come back, Bruce? A Stick.

PUZZLE 85
No. 7.

PUZZLE 86
Across: 1. Plane, 4. Brace and Bit, 6. Mallet, 8. Chisel, 10. Hammer.
Down: 1. Punch, 2. Nails, 3. Screwdriver, 5. Rule, 7. Pliers, 8. Clamp, 9. Saw.

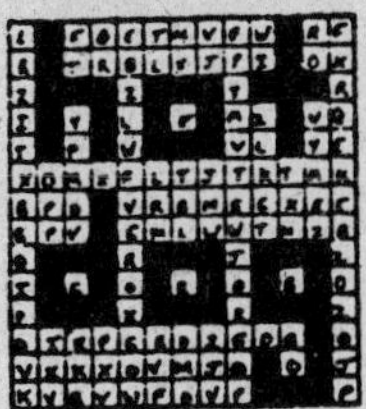

PUZZLE 87

PUZZLE 88

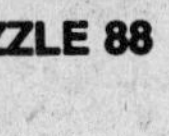

PUZZLE 89

PUZZLE 90

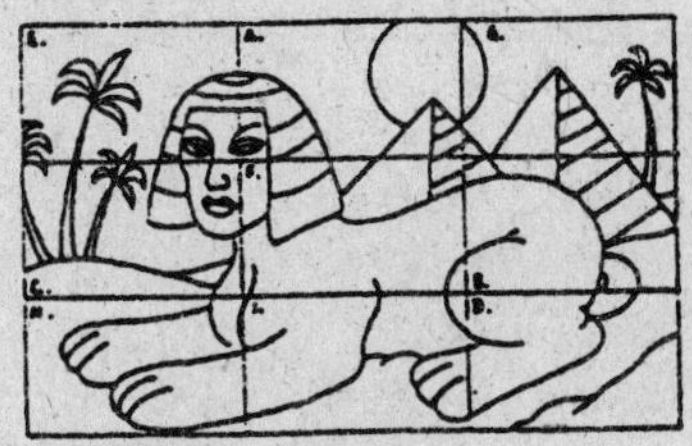

PUZZLE 92

PUZZLE 93

6B, 10C, 1B, 4D, 10K, 13F, 4L.

SOLUTIONS

PUZZLE 94

PUZZLE 95

1–5, 3–4, 2–6.

PUZZLE 96

Penguin, Iceberg, Cockerel, Nose, Igloo, Cat = Picnic.
Pot, Aeroplane, Rain, Tap, Yacht = Party.

PUZZLE 97

10+20	210302
25-22	5630IC
64+36	638100
71-20	27515!
83+21	810421
62-52	565210
49+6	55943
17+17	77342
13-6	37924

PUZZLE 98

PUZZLE 99

PUZZLE 100

3 and 14.

PUZZLE 101

PUZZLE 102

PUZZLE 103

PUZZLE 104

SOLUTIONS

PUZZLE 105

PUZZLE 106

A and F.

PUZZLE 107

PUZZLE 108

The Sun, all the rest of the objects have 4 letters in their name.

PUZZLE 110

PUZZLE 111

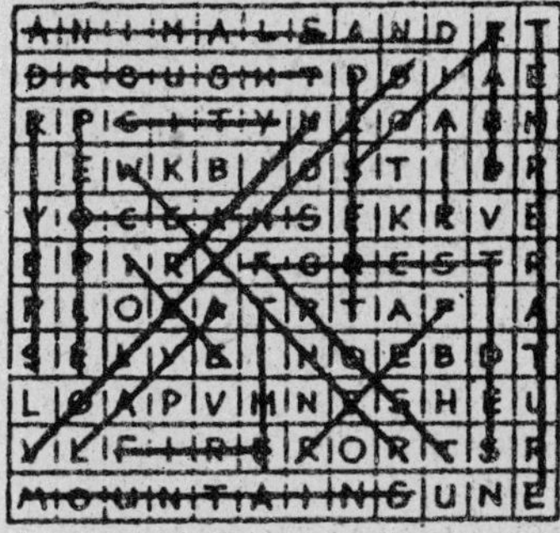

PUZZLE 112

3. 16, 4. J.

PUZZLE 113

Horns.

PUZZLE 115

Detail D.

PUZZLE 114

SOLUTIONS

PUZZLE 116

PUZZLE 118

5, 3, 7, 1, 6, 2, 4, 9, 8.

PUZZLE 119

Jelly, cat, sock, duck, scarf, iceberg, choirboy, trousers, flowerpot - JACK FROST.

PUZZLE 121

Blackboard, Chalk, Teacher, Classroom.

PUZZLE 122

1–F, 2–C, 3–D, 4–B, 5–A, 6–E.

PUZZLE 123

PUZZLE 124

A–6, B–1, C–5, D–2, E–4, F–3.

PUZZLE 125

PUZZLE 126

30 balloons.

PUZZLE 127

Across: 3.Medicine, 4. Tablet, 5. Thermometer, 6. Cap, 8. Meal.
Down: 1. Uniform, 2. Stethoscope, 7. Pills.

PUZZLE 128

A–F, B–E, C–D.

PUZZLE 129

Route 7.

SOLUTIONS

PUZZLE 130

PUZZLE 131

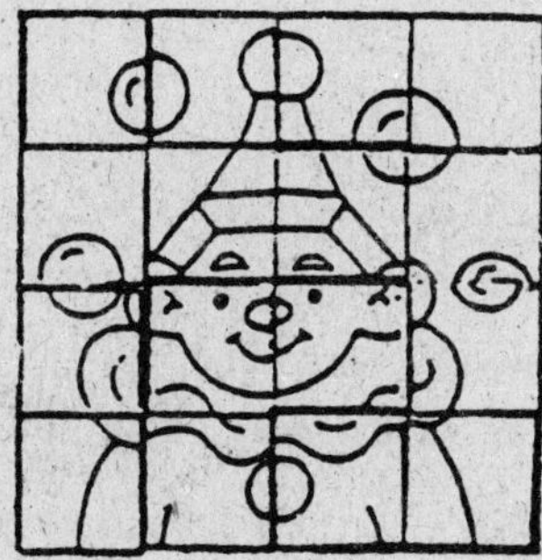

PUZZLE 132

Piece B.

PUZZLE 133

Detail A

PUZZLE 134

Archibald.

PUZZLE 135

PUZZLE 137

PUZZLE 138

A2, B1, C2, D1, E1, F2, G1, H2, I1, J2.

PUZZLE 140

PUZZLE 142

Across: 1. Letters, 3. Loaf, 4. Tree, 5. Acorn, 8. Leek, 9. Pins, 11. Stool.
Down: 2. Tea, 3. Leaves, 6. Rope, 7. Glass, 10. Knot.

PUZZLE 143

Vine No. 3.

PUZZLE 144

Plant, Bottle, Lamp, Cook Book, Cup.

SOLUTIONS

PUZZLE 145

O	M	S	S	B
T	O	H	T	I
T	U	R	O	S
E	S	E	A	O
R	E	W	T	N

PUZZLE 148

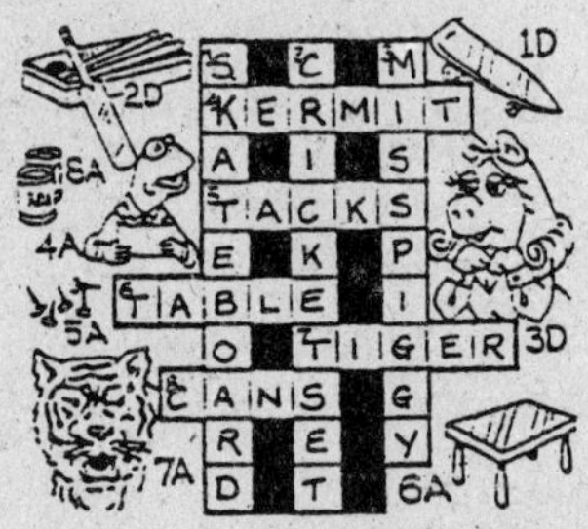

PUZZLE 149

2 and 7.

PUZZLE 146
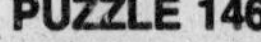

PUZZLE 150

4 and 7.

PUZZLE 151

PUZZLE 147

PUZZLE 152

SOLUTIONS

PUZZLE 153

PUZZLE 154

1–E, 2–C, 3–A, 4–F, 5–D, 6–B.

PUZZLE 155

PUZZLE 156

I'm great at solving puzzles in the Junior Puzzle Book.

PUZZLE 157

1-2-4-2-4-5-9-3.

PUZZLE 158

Eggs, bacon, sausage, ham, tomatoes, mushrooms, porridge, cornflakes, beans, toast.

PUZZLE 159

A-c, B-a, C-d, D-b.

PUZZLE 160

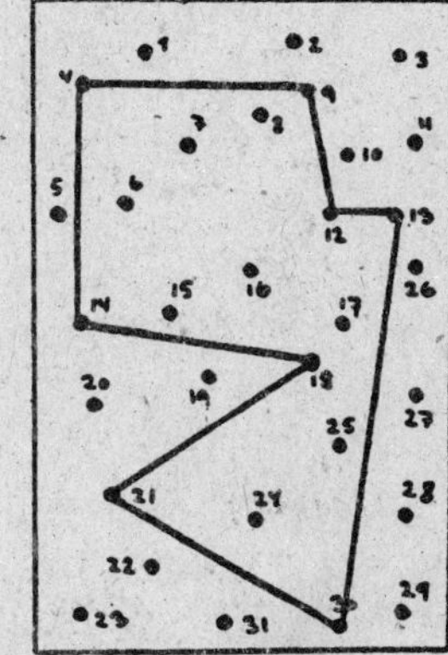

PUZZLE 161

PUZZLE 163

No. 3.

SOLUTIONS

PUZZLE 164

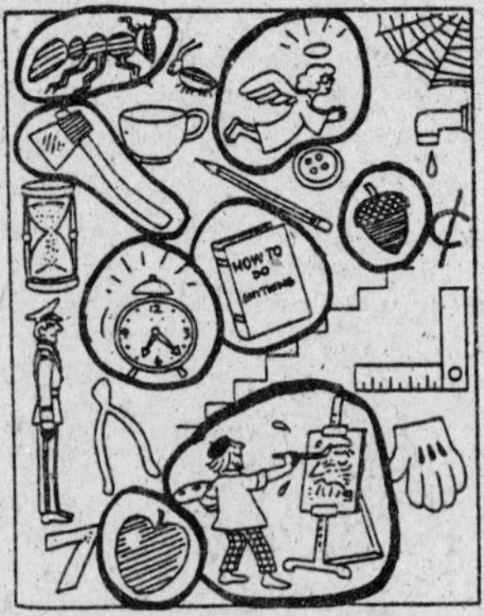

PUZZLE 165

PUZZLE 166

Mary.

PUZZLE 167

Pictures 2 and 5.

PUZZLE 168

Mark, Paul, Steven, Stuart.

PUZZLE 169

PUZZLE 170

PUZZLE 171

Pictures 5 and 8.

SOLUTIONS

PUZZLE 172

A3, B4, C1 and D2.

PUZZLE 173

23 leaves.

PUZZLE 174

40 squares.

PUZZLE 175

PUZZLE 176

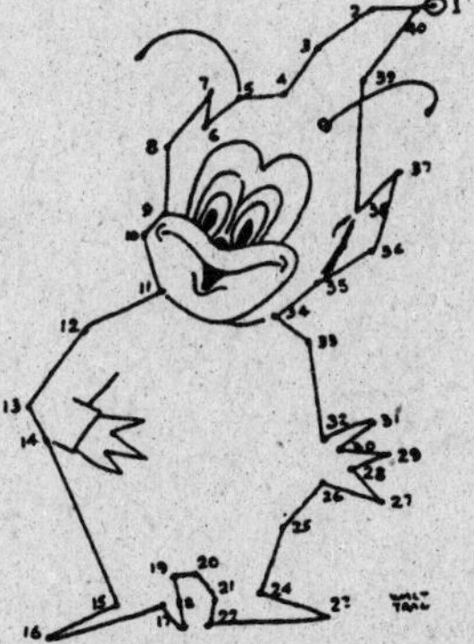

PUZZLE 177

Nail (Sail), Pear (Chair), Tie (Eye), Pen (Ten), Can (Fan), Egg (Peg), Hat (Mat), Nose (Rose).

PUZZLE 178

PUZZLE 180

11 items.

PUZZLE 181

SOLUTIONS

PUZZLE 182

Shadow B.

PUZZLE 183

PUZZLE 184

PUZZLE 185

A3, B4, C1, D2.

PUZZLE 186

Giraffe, Mallard, Lapwing, Gorilla, Dolphin, Gazelle, Leopard, Moorhen.

PUZZLE 187

Picture No. 10.

PUZZLE 188

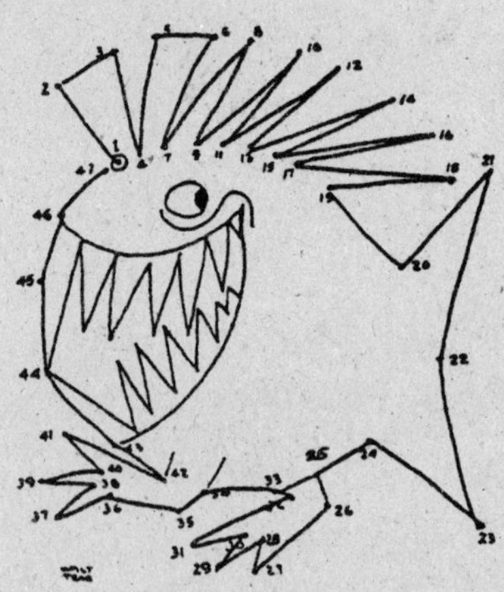

PUZZLE 189

PUZZLE 190

Numbers, 1, 2, 7, 11, 16.